THE
SOMERSET WETLANDS
An Ever Changing Environment

**Editors: Dr Pat Hill-Cottingham, Derek Briggs,
Richard Brunning, Dr Andy King, Graham Rix**

First published in Great Britain in 2006
Reprinted 2008

British Library Cataloguing-in-Publication Data
A CIP record for this title is available from the British Library

ISBN 978 0 86183 432 7

In partnership with

Somerset Archaeological and Natural History Society

Somerset Books is a partnership between
DAA Halsgrove Ltd and Somerset County Council
(Directorate of Culture and Heritage)
www.somerset.gov.uk

Halsgrove House
Ryelands Industrial Estate, Bagley Road,
Wellington, Somerset TA21 9PZ
Tel: 01823 653777
Fax: 01823 216796
email: sales@halsgrove.com
website: www.halsgrove.com

Printed and bound by Grafiche Flaminia, Italy

Contents

Acknowledgements

First of all the editors wish to thank all the writers who have contributed to the variety and interest in this book with so much enthusiasm and willingness. They would also like to thank the following individuals and groups - often unsung heroes behind the scenes, who have given valuable advice and help:

Members of the Somerset Levels Project, A. Alderton, S. Beckett, A. Caseldine, M. Girling, F. Hibbert and R. Housley, also N. Cameron, S. Haslett, F. Chambers, P. Davies, D. Druce, R. Housley, H. Kenward, J. Jones, M. Robinson, H. Tinsley, D. Smith, V. Straker , K. Wilkinson and R. McDonnell, led by John and Bryony Coles

Help and advice was also received from David Ballance, Phil Holms, Professor Christopher McGowan, Dr Allan Morton (DMAPW), Stephen Parker, Tony Price (for distribution maps produced using DMAPW), Brian Gibson, David Reid and James Williams. Maps and geological profiles were contributed by Derek Briggs, drawings of aquatic organisms by Susan Hill-Cottingham and birds by Derek Briggs, Kathryn Eales for supplying fossil *S. nitida* and Dr Alisa Watson for supplying the Pevensey specimen.

Acknowledgements are also due to the NERC Satellite Station, University of Dundee (climate map in *The storm of 1990*), Somerset Environmental Records Centre (digital aerial map images of Sharpham Moor Plot and supply of John Boyd slides), the *Polden Post* (The Shapwick Giant), Coates Willows and Wetlands Visitors Centre (photographs illustrating the story of willow), Somerset County Museum (pictures of ammonites in its published book *Fossil Ammonites from the Somerset Coast),* Somerset Record Society (historic maps) and to Mrs C Boyd for permission to use her late husband's photographs.

Supporting the whole project were members of Somerset Archaeological and Natural History Society Natural History Committee (David Ballance, Derek Briggs, Russell Gomm, Pat Hill-Cottingham, Simon Leach, Philip Radford, Graham Rix and Tony Sergeant), and Publications Committee (Anthony Bruce, Angela Dix, Peter Ellis, Dennis Hill-Cottingham, Pat Hill-Cottingham, Barry Lane, Tom Mayberry and Jill Polak). Especial thanks are due to Tom Mayberry for invaluable advice on many historical points.

Last but by no means least we thank all our proof readers, including John and Pat Gale and Dennis Hill-Cottingham and the copy editor Peter Ellis.

PHOTOGRAPHS

Photographs were supplied by Dr Mark Anderson, Dr Peter Beeden, Dave Beszant (Sedgemoor District Council), the late John Boyd, Jayne Brayne, Derek Briggs, Richard Brunning, Dr Pat Hill-Cottingham, K Crabtree, Francis Farr-Cox, A. Forrestier, Keith Gould, Phil Holms, Sally Mills, Lynne Newton, Dr Michael Proctor, Dr Philip Radford, Tom Raven, Dr Stephen Rippon, Graham Rix, Geoff Roberts, Roger Rogers, David Sheppard, Bernard Storer, Vanessa Straker, John M Walters, Robin Williams, Eddie Wills.

We also used the archives of the Somerset Archaeological and Natural History Society, Somerset Levels Project, Somerset County Council Historic Services, Somerset Record Society, Royal Society for the Protection of Birds and English Nature.

The Somerset Archaeological and Natural History Society wishes to acknowledge the financial support of English Nature, The Environment Agency, The Bristol Naturalists' Society, Somerset County Council, Sedgemoor District Council, Taunton Deane Borough Council, The Levels and Moors Partnership, the Royal Society for the Protection of Birds, Leader+. We also had donations from R. Cox, W.J.Ingles and Anon, and an interest-free loan from the Geologists' Association.

Somerset Wetlands –
An ever-changing environment

Prof. Mick Aston

It is a pleasure to welcome this volume on the Somerset wetlands and to be asked to write a fore-word for it. This is the first time that the Somerset wetlands, an internationally important Ramsar site, has had a full academic appraisal.

When I first came to live in Somerset over thirty years ago I was immediately immensely impressed by the flat floodable lands in the centre of the county. Apart from the fantastic archaeology in the Levels, which was being examined at the time by John and Bryony Coles and their team, I liked the open 'wildness' of the place. Although local Somerset people value the landscape of the Levels, they have never attracted the same attention as the uplands have – Exmoor, Mendip and the Quantocks. Why is it that invariably the mountains and upland parts of the country are made National Parks or Areas of Outstanding Natural Beauty?

This volume will help to redress the balance. It is truly a multi-disciplinary study, reflected in the disci-plines of the five editors. For the first time the inter-relationships between geology, archaeology, history, flora and fauna in the Levels is explained. It should provide a sound base for research in future, given the problems we all face with changing climate. I recommend it whole-heartedly.

Opposite page: Roe Deer. GR

Heron. RW

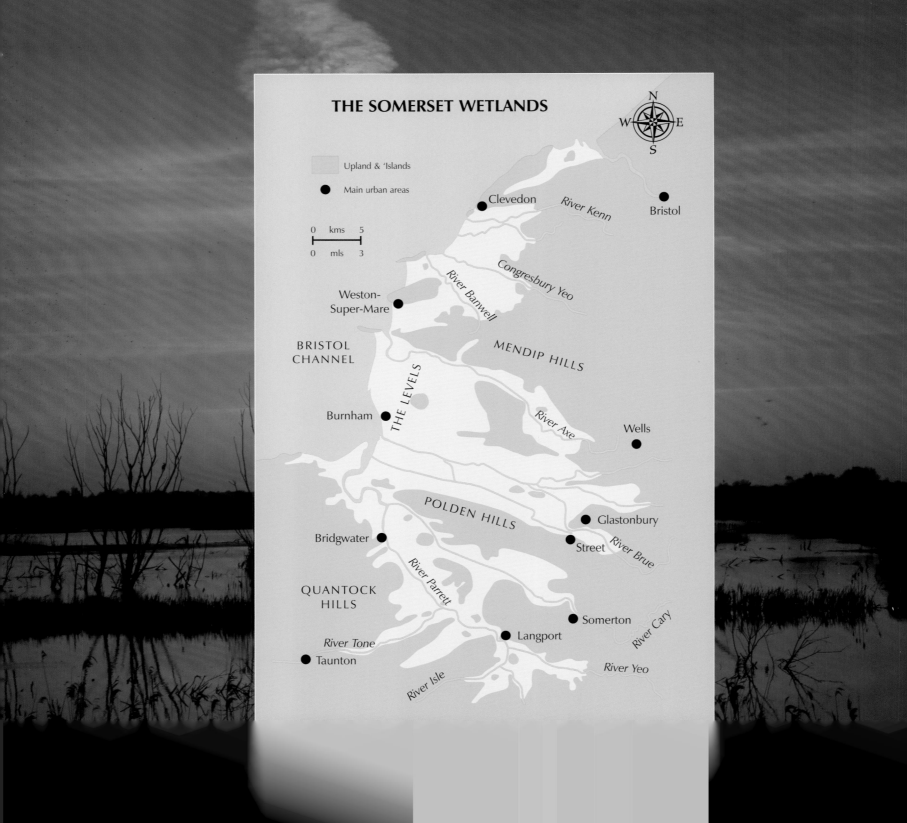

THE SOMERSET WETLANDS

Upland & 'Islands

● Main urban areas

0 kms 5
0 mls 3

N
W E
S

Clevedon

Bristol

River Kenn

Congresbury Yeo

River Banwell

Weston-
Super-Mare

BRISTOL
CHANNEL

MENDIP HILLS

THE LEVELS

Burnham

River Axe

Wells

POLDEN HILLS

Glastonbury

Bridgwater

Street

River Brue

River Parrett

QUANTOCK
HILLS

Somerton

River Cary

River Tone

Langport

Taunton

River Isle

River Yeo

Setting the Scene

Bernard Storer

About six thousand years ago, when the land had 'settled down', following a long period of flooding, humans were putting the land, its plants and animals, to their own use. Much is now known of the pre-history of the Levels and Moors and the illustration on page 17 shows a reconstruction of one of the earliest trackways, the Sweet Track at Westhay, built in 3806 BC to enable Neolithic man to cross the marshes separating the upland Meare island from the Polden Hills. A full scale replica can be seen at the Peat Moors Centre, which also houses some of the artefacts found along the Sweet Track.

Information from archaeology, from pollen grain analysis and from our knowledge of plant succession gives us a picture of the land at that time. The dominant vegetation over much of the Levels was a reed/sedge swamp but, in the area between the Poldens and the Wedmore ridge, a more acidic heath developed. The presence of this type of heath vegetation is reflected in the place names that we still use – for example Shapwick Heath and Westhay Heath. Because the peat soil was apparent at the surface, this is the area generally known as the Peat Moors.

The people of that time were the first farmers who were beginning to make clearances in the dry-land forests for their crops and domesticated animals.

Our first evidence that humans had started to dig out peat, dry it and use it as a fuel, comes from its use on the Roman period salt-making sites. Mediaeval records show that it was a well-established practice by that time. Clearly this started as a simple manual job and this method continued, relatively unchanged, until the 1950s.

Teasels originally grown for carding wool. LN

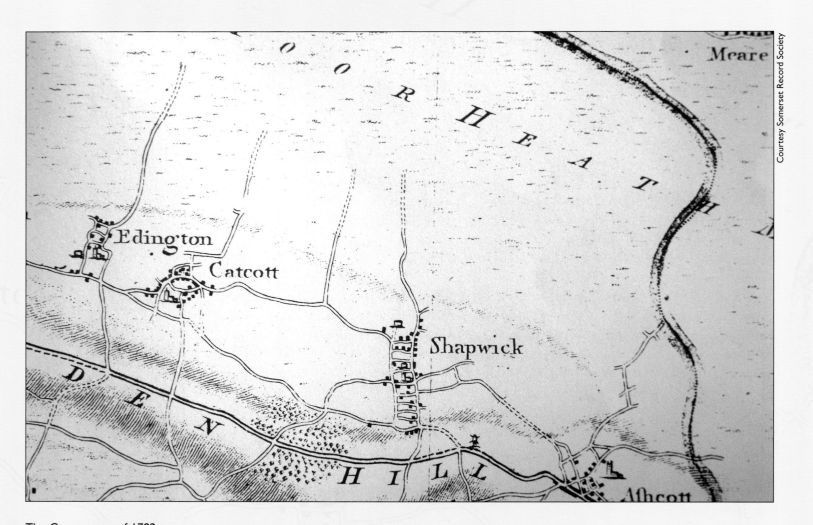

The County map of 1782

This long period with little change is emphasised on the County map of 1782 which shows that the roads, paths and droves running north from the Polden villages petered out after about a mile – there was still no through road across the peat moors. It was only in the early nineteenth century, after the widespread drainage pattern we see today was constructed, that road links were established between the Poldens and Wedmore.

When I first started to look at the area, in the 1950s, the common pattern for much of the Levels and Moors was for the land to be used for summer grazing only as it was frequently flooded in winter. On the peat moors a more mixed farming pattern developed. A fairly typical farm, held a few cows, a handful of pigs, various hens and geese and about half an acre was given over to vegetables and, in summer, an area was dug for peat. This was peat extraction on a small local scale. Young boys in the area rarely did a paper round before school! Instead they used a bucket and pole device to drain a section of the peat trench which their fathers would be cutting later in the day. A few of the older generation still refer to themselves as peat farmers.

Whilst there were a number of the small peat farmers, one or two families were giving up their farming interests and concentrating on peat extraction. Whether the peat was being dug by small or large operators, the result was a landscape that was covered in ruckles. Ruckles were the stacks of drying peat blocks; each ruckle was about four or five feet high and the shape of an old-fashioned bee hive. Such ruckles would be built up of several hundreds of blocks. Once the peat was dry, it could be taken away by cart, by barge, or, in my day, a local pick-up truck that delivered to nearby villages.

By the end of the 1950s, one family in particular saw the possibility of marketing peat for horticultural use. They already had a light railway which carried the peat from the field ruckles to a central depot. It was here that they built a shed where peat could be ground into the crumbly texture beloved by gardeners. But gardeners also wanted their peat to be moist. Dry peat blocks could be stored or transported in the open without any problems but damp, crumbly peat would quickly rot the hessian sacks which were the standard containers of that time. However, the plastics industry was beginning to take off and the black plastic bag was an ideal container for this horticultural peat. The first black plastic bags that I ever saw were at these Ashcott works.

Bernard Storer and Olive Hallam recording plants at Catcott Heath Reserve.

GR

Early use of plastic for peat sacks

Modern peat machine

Following a very successful marketing campaign, the sale of horticultural peat began to rocket. To keep pace with demand, large peat-cutting machines were introduced, more efficient pumps were brought in and, in a few years, the rate of peat extraction was such that as much peat was taken out between 1960 and 1970 as in the previous one hundred years. Not only was the extraction rate increased but the digging was no longer a small scale operation and it became a 'big business', all year round operation.

As far back as 1923, a few scientists had recognised the ecological importance of the peat moors and, through the efforts of the Society for the Promotion of Nature Conservation (later the Royal Society for Nature Conservation and now known simply as the Wildlife Trusts) a small nature reserve had been established on Sharpham Moor .

On the conservation front, little happened during the next forty or so years; but the increase in the rate of peat extraction, and therefore habitat changes, did alert a small group of people. The Nature Conservation Council (now English Nature) was hampered then by lack of funds but was able to negotiate a lease over part of Shapwick Heath.

BS

BS

BS

Above: Southern Marsh Orchid.

Top middle: Marsh Pea.

Top right: Bog Asphodel.

Right: Raft Spider

GR

In the early 1970s, the Somerset Trust for Nature Conservation (now Somerset Wildlife Trust) was able to purchase two reserves, one at Catcott and one at Westhay. Whilst peat extraction was stopped on the reserves, changes in the surrounding habitat were still taking place. The new peat extraction programme meant that the reserves were, literally, being left high and dry. Not only was more and more water being pumped from deeper and deeper cuts but there was no winter rest when the extraction stopped and the winter rain allowed the water level to recover.

This drying out meant that entire habitats could disappear. Depressions, normally filled with water and sphagnum moss, were being lost and with them the associated fauna such as the Marsh Grasshopper and Raft Spider. Dragonfly and damselfly species were losing the aquatic habitat essential for their larval development, unusual plants such as Sundew and Royal Fern were becoming scarcer, as were waders such as Snipe.

In an attempt to halt the habitat loss, the conservation bodies mounted their own campaign to try to persuade people to cut back on their use of peat. At the same time, the STNC held meetings with representatives of Fisons (who by that time had become major land owners) and suggested that their working programme should be managed in such a way that a moat would be created around the reserves, e.g. Westhay Moor. This moat would act to pen back the natural rainfall which would fall on to the reserve and stop it from being pumped away. It was then suggested that the moat would become an aquatic habitat in its own right and that it should be managed as part of the reserve.

Whilst these plans were being made, Fisons was succeeded by Levingtons and they responded to persuasion, both locally and nationally, to reduce peat extraction. Eventually they gave, not just enough land for a moat, but enough to enable SWT to create what became Westhay National Nature Reserve.

At Catcott, a similar arrangement with private land owners allowed the Trust to expand a small reserve into what we now call the Catcott Reserve Complex, which includes Catcott Heath, Catcott North, Catcott South and Catcott Lows.

Whilst the Trust was establishing Westhay and Catcott, EN was creating the Shapwick Heath with its own ponds, reed beds, meadows and wet woodland. This was followed by the Royal Society for the

PHC

Royal Fern *Osmunda regalis*.

Opposite page: Snipe. RW

Opposite page:
The Sweet Track 3806BC.
G. MORTLEMANS

Black tailed Godwit.

Protection of Birds (RSPB) setting up a similar reserve at Ham Wall. This pattern of bringing land into both direct and indirect conservation management is still continuing although the pace of change has slowed down.

Although the conservationists can claim success, particularly in the variety and numbers of birds which can now be seen, Bittern, Ruff, Godwit, Goosander and duck species, we must remember that much of the heath habitat of the 1950s and 1960s has disappeared. No longer are Nightjars a 'certainty' and of the habitat that is left, much of it is very fragile, and the plants which attracted the early naturalists, Marsh Pea, Saw Sedge, Bladderwort, as well as the other plants of the fen meadows, are still in need of protection. We must do all in our power to ensure that this rare habitat with its unique wildlife is still there for future generations.

RW

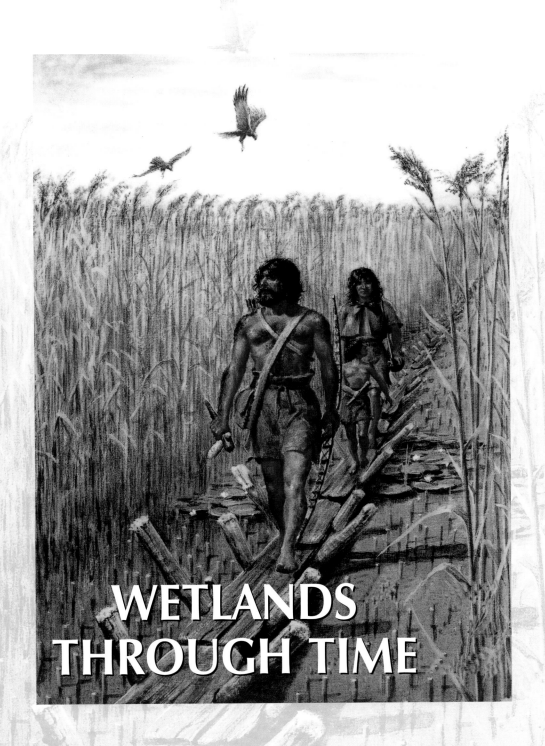

WETLANDS
THROUGH TIME

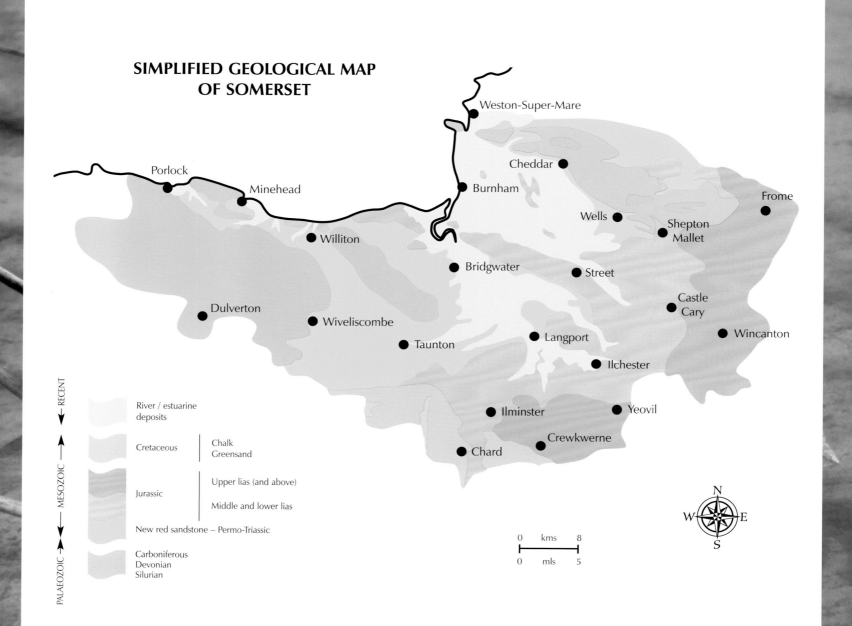

SIMPLIFIED GEOLOGICAL MAP
OF SOMERSET

Weston-Super-Mare

Porlock

Minehead

Cheddar

Burnham

Frome

Wells

Shepton
Mallet

Williton

Bridgwater

Street

Dulverton

Wiveliscombe

Castle
Cary

Taunton

Langport

Wincanton

Ilchester

Ilminster

Yeovil

Crewkwerne

Chard

RECENT

River / estuarine
deposits

Cretaceous

Chalk
Greensand

MESOZOIC

Jurassic

Upper lias (and above)

Middle and lower lias

New red sandstone – Permo-Triassic

PALAEOZOIC

Carboniferous
Devonian
Silurian

| 0 | kms | 8 |
| 0 | mls | 5 |

N
W   E
S

Beneath Your Feet – The geological foundations of the Somerset Wetlands

Derek Briggs, Dennis Parsons and Andy King

The rocks within and framing the Somerset Wetlands provide clues to several very different environments and striking changes in climate which have existed in this area during the past 400 million years. The diverse range of rocks and fossils provide evidence for the former presence of seas, forests, volcanoes, deserts and ice sheets.

The oldest local rocks form the Quantock Hills and the core of the Mendip Ridge. Though now solid purple-red sandstones and siltstones, 400 million years ago they were sands and gravels being deposited in the deltas of huge rivers which crossed the area from the north. A few fossil shellfish and simple plant remains found in these rocks indicate the coastal position and the arid harsh climate that existed in these Devonian times.

This harsh, dry landscape changed about 355 million years ago when the sea advanced northwards and layers of carbonate silts and muds accumulated on the sea floor. Over time these sediments hardened to form the grey Carboniferous Limestones which are so characteristic of the Mendip Hills and provide some of the most dramatic scenery in Somerset such as Cheddar Gorge, Ebbor Gorge and Burrington Combe. Apart from yielding huge quantities of roadstone from vast mechanised quarries, the Carboniferous Limestone is usually very fossiliferous containing shells, corals and crinoids. Judging from their modern counterparts, the ancient sea was tropical, warm and shallow.

Near Weston-super-Mare, the Carboniferous Limestones contain volcanic lavas. These exhibit rounded 'pillow-shaped' lava flows typical of quieter underwater eruptions as well as fragmented explosive material.

GR

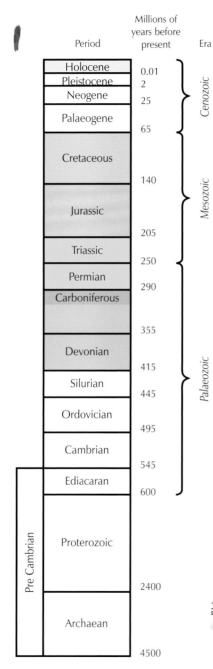

Period	Millions of years before present	Era
Holocene	0.01	
Pleistocene	2	
Neogene	25	Cenozoic
Palaeogene	65	
Cretaceous	140	
Jurassic	205	Mesozoic
Triassic	250	
Permian	290	
Carboniferous	355	
Devonian	415	
Silurian	445	Palaeozoic
Ordovician	495	
Cambrian	545	
Ediacaran	600	
Proterozoic	2400	Pre Cambrian
Archaean	4500	

Some 50 million years later the shallow sea had become choked with deltaic sediments which in turn provided the perfect environment for extensive tropical forests and humid swamps. These were colonised by luxuriant tree ferns and large club-mosses, a habitat in which some of the earliest amphibians and the largest dragonflies (with 60cm wingspan) lived! The fallen fragments of trees and ferns accumulated and formed peat deposits which, ultimately, became the coal seams of the late Carboniferous 'coal measures'. This 'Somerset Coalfield' was worked just north of the Mendip Hills around Radstock in the 19th and 20th centuries.

The next events in the geological history had a profound impact and literally shaped the framework of our present landscape. Around 300 million years ago the inexorable processes of continental drift finally brought two ancient super-continents, Gondwana and Laurasia into a collision contact. All the strata so far deposited were crushed, folded and fractured to form a series of high hills and deep valleys. The degraded and eroded remains of two of these hill ranges form the present day Mendip and Quantock Hills – it is estimated that when first formed these hills may have been up to three-times higher than at present. The original broad and relatively flat-bottomed intervening valley under-lies the wetlands of central Somerset.

Similarly, north of Mendip, two narrower but still severe downfolds created ancient valleys which now underlie the Wrington and Nailsea lowlands.

GEOLOGICAL SECTION RELATING GEOLOGY TO LANDSCAPE
Mendip Hills – Quantock Hills

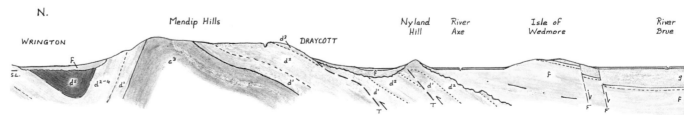

As soon as hills are created they become subject to erosion by wind, frost, rain, ice, rivers and the sea. Rock fragments and soils are transported downhill so the hill crests become lower and the valleys gradually become infilled with sediment.

The first sediments filling the lowest parts of the newly created lowlands were red – this is a colour typically associated with sub-aerial oxidation of iron minerals and is characteristic of arid climates. Against the bounding slopes of the ancient Mendip and Quantock Hills are coarse fossil scree and wadi-floor sediments. Associated red sandstones often show sedimentary features interpreted as fossil sand dune structures. The overlying red mudstones probably formed as wind-blown dust trapped in temporary shallow lakes or ponds. Beneath Brent Knoll and the Polden Hills these rocks contain layers of halite or 'rock salt' produced by evaporation. Fossils are very scarce – and usually represented by the occasional reptilian bone. All these 'Permo-Triassic' rocks of over 200 million years ago, were evidently formed in tropical desert or semi-desert conditions.

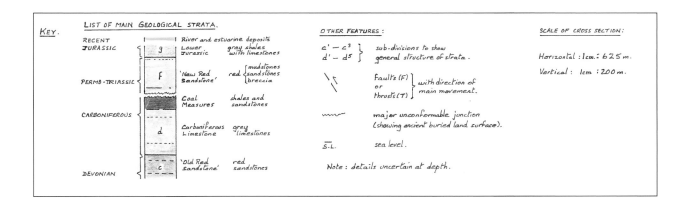

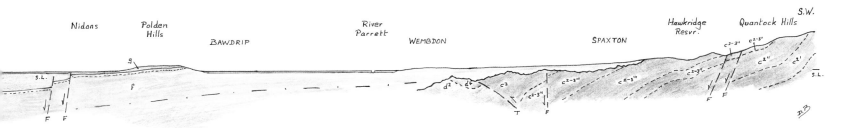

Jurassic seascape.

Quite abruptly the red rocks are overlain by grey shales, mudstones and muddy limestones. They may be glimpsed near Wedmore and on the Polden Hills where the limestone often weathers to a yellow colour and is a popular building material on account of its tabular and flat form. These rocks are often packed with a rich variety of fossil shellfish (especially ammonites – a type of extinct marine mollusc) and are well known for the fossil remains of large, streamlined reptiles such as ichthyosaurs and long-necked plesiosaurs. All these fossils are marine and they indicate a rapid flooding of the previous desert landscape by the Jurassic sea about 200 million years ago. Increased humidity is also indicated by fossilised fragments of land plants which, as waterlogged driftwood, became trapped in the marine sediments. It seems that they were washed off what were by then the local Mendip and Quantock islands!

Gilling Down showing the contrast between the red and grey strata.

A small ichthyosaur collected from Kilve beach by staff from the County Museum and English Nature.

Excavation of the plesiosaur from the fore-shore at Hinkley Point in 2003.

SOMERSET 'SEA DRAGONS' AND DINOSAURS

Quarrying of the lower Jurassic ('Blue Lias') flagstones around Glastonbury and Street during the eighteenth and nineteenth centuries revealed the existence of fossil skeletons of large reptiles. Early naturalists interpreted these as fish, lizards or even 'sea-dragons'.

Today we recognise these fossils as those of predatory, air-breathing marine reptiles, called ichthyosaurs and plesiosaurs, and these were the top-carnivores in the early Jurassic seas which covered the Somerset wetlands approximately 190 to 200 million years ago.

The name *'ichthyosaurus'* literally means 'fish-lizard'. They were marine reptiles with a shark- or dolphin-like shape. Most appear to have been adapted for fast cruising and some may have been endothermic. Their large eyes and long narrow snouts lined with sharp pointed teeth, indicate that they were active predators and their stomach contents show that they fed on marine squid (belemnites), fish, ammonites and even smaller ichthyosaurs. They were highly advanced reptiles, and gave birth to live young just like dolphins do today. The lifespan of ichthyosaurs is not known. However, modern sharks and small whales can live for 30-35 years and since these animals occupied similar ecological niches, perhaps ichthyosaurs lived for comparable periods. So many ichthyosaurs were found around Street, that the town adopted an image of the fossil skeleton as its logo – this can still be seen on the local road signs!

The first plesiosaur fossil was discovered by the famous collector, Mary Anning of Lyme Regis, in the winter of 1820-1821. She sold it to a fossil collector, who in turn lent it to the Revd. William Conybeare to study. He named this new group of marine reptiles 'plesiosaurs' – derived from the Greek meaning 'near reptile'. Plesiosaurs were carnivorous marine reptiles like ichthyosaurs – but they possessed flattened bodies, with two pairs of paddles and a long neck at the end of which was a small head armed with a fearsome array of curved, sharp teeth. They were powerful and highly manoeuver-able swimmers.

Quarrying for 'Blue Lias' flagstones has long-since ceased in the vicinity of Street and Glastonbury and today fossil ichthyosaurs and plesiosaurs are usually found on the Somerset coast between Blue Anchor and Stolford. Although isolated rib or vertebrae fossils are fairly common, complete skeletons are rare and a new discovery is always exciting! In 2003 a complete plesiosaur skeleton was discovered on the beach in Bridgwater Bay National Nature Reserve. This fossil is now undergoing conservation and study and is planned to be on display in Taunton Castle Museum next year.

Apart from fossil marine 'sea-dragons', Somerset also had its own 'land-living dragons' – or dinosaurs! In 1893, the Revd Hervey, vicar of Wedmore parish, heard of the discovery of bones by local workmen and asked his brother-in-law, William Sanford of Nynhead Court, Wellington, to recover the fossils. The disarticulated limb bones, ribs and skull fragments turned out to be the fossil remains of Somerset's only known dinosaurs, *Camalotia* and *Avalonia*, which are now being conserved at the Natural History Museum, London.

Dennis Parsons

FOSSIL AMMONITES

Ammonites have long been regarded as one of the most popular groups of fossils, and Somerset, especially the coast, is a favourite 'hunting ground' for many fossil enthusiasts. They have a special place in local Somerset folklore.

Legend has it that Saint Keyna, the daughter of Prince Brychan of Gwent (Breckonshire), came to a Somerset Saxon town as a Welsh missionary and asked to build a dwelling in the nearby woods. The local chief tried to dissuade Keyna by telling her that the place swarmed with serpents, however on her undertaking that she would rid the place of the venomous creatures she was allowed to stay. Keyna devoted herself to missionary work and through her prayers she turned the snakes into stone (ammonites) and made the woods safe – hence Keynsham (Keyna's ham) was named.

Ammonites are an extinct group of marine molluscs – related to squids, cuttlefish, octopuses and the Indo-Pacific *Nautilus*. They had coiled shells, divided into chambers separated by partitions which strengthened the shell and prevented it from being crushed by the pressure of the surrounding sea-water. The external surface of the shell was often ornamented by growth lines or straight or curved 'ribs'; the exact form of this ornament is very important for identifying different types of ammonites. Similarly the outline of the shell edge, for example, rounded, angular or flattened, is a useful distinguishing feature. The ammonite head was surrounded by a ring of muscular tentacles and the whole body was contained in the last-formed part of the shell, nearest the opening. Chambers nearer the centre of the coil were filled with varying amounts of gas and liquid which the animal could control to allow it to rise or sink through the water column (similar to the operation of ballast tanks in a submarine!)

Ammonites probably fed on plankton, small crustaceans, shells and corals – they may have also browsed on sea-floor vegetation and scavenged the bodies of dead sea creatures.

Study of the ammonites in a rock sequence in one area quickly demonstrates that they are not evenly distributed; species appear and disappear as progressively younger rocks are examined. Because they evolved so quickly, were extremely common, widespread and diverse, and had hard shells which fossilise relatively easily, ammonites make ideal zone fossils – they are some of the most important and best indicators for arranging rocks in order of age.

True ammonites appeared at the beginning of the Jurassic Period, about 200 million years ago and occur in the early Jurassic mudstones and limestones beneath the Somerset wetlands and in the surrounding hills. Some of the earliest forms of ammonites were described from Somerset, from the foreshore exposures near Watchet. They declined and eventually became extinct about 65 million years ago, at approximately the same time that dinosaurs disappeared from the land.

Andy King

Psiloceras.

Diagram of ammonite reconstruction.

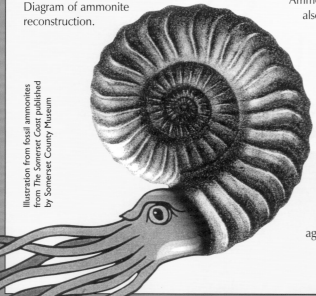

The Jurassic sea eventually drowned even these uplands. Subsequently, its muddy waters cleared to allow the deposition of a very pure and fossiliferous fine white calcareous deposit largely made of plates from innumerable minute algae. This formed in Cretaceous times, between about 140 and 65 million years ago and hardened into the Chalk rock; its nearest occurrence now is in the Windwhistle and Blackdown Hills of south Somerset.

Local proof of events for the next 60 million years or so is scanty, and geological deposits of this period found elsewhere are missing here. It seems that erosive processes became dominant again, and certainly they have cut deeply into the pre-existing layers of Chalk, Jurassic and Triassic strata, leaving only a tattered and patchy record for geologists to interpret. The isolated outcrops of Brent Knoll and Glastonbury Tor exemplify the latter. The relative softness of these sediments has guided the erosive actions of present rivers to partly re-reveal the nearly 300 million year old valleys between the older and harder Mendip and Quantock Hills, and North and South of North Hill (Bristol Airport).

During the several cold and warm Pleistocene 'Ice Age' climates of the last 2 million years, a variety of animals and people has attempted to colonise this ancient landscape. Some of them are just as unexpected as their fossil predecessors. Local fossils of this age include mammoths, woolly rhinos, cave bear and bison of the colder periods, and lions, hyaenas and prehistoric elephants of warmer ones. The caves and fissures where their remains were found also give evidence of early human activity. One of the oldest records of human presence in Britain comes from flint artefacts found at Westbury Quarry which are dated to about 500 000 years ago (Cromerian). Other evidence of cave dwelling humans is found at Cheddar and Wookey Hole.

Although the ice-sheets seem never to have covered this area, the climatic fluctuations clearly affected the amount of water locked up in the ice. During glacial periods mean sea level was much lower than now; flint artefacts and fossil soils, tree stumps and trunks are occasionally exposed at low tide along the coast ,as at Stolford near Hinkley Point. In the warmest periods the sea rose to or above present levels; raised beach features lie up to 14 metres above today's mean sea level along the Clevedon-Brean Down coast. Many of the steepest wetland margins are in fact, ancient 'fossil' cliff lines.

Within the Somerset wetlands near Middlezoy and Burtle and also at Kenn, near Clevedon, there are low mounds of shelly sands and gravels which contain a modern mixed marine and freshwater fauna

A fossil seed-fern

Part of a leaf of *Alethopteris*, a seed-fern (pteridosperm) from the late carboniferous (coal measures) swamp-forests of c.300 million years ago. Unlike contemporaneous and modern ferns, these plants reproduced by large seeds rather than sporangia. In the early twentieth century, seed-ferns were the first totally extinct group of plants to be recognised in the fossil record. This specimen was found in the N Somerset coalfield near Radstock .

Derek Briggs

of limpets, mussels, cockles and gastropods. They are believed to represent sand-banks formed during one of the higher interglacial sea-levels.

The detailed history of the last 10 000 years of the Somerset Wetlands is dealt with in other sections of this book, but the last chapter of this geological story covers the accumulation and formation of the wetland peat deposits and associated sediments. The main peat accumulation originated about 6 000 years ago in mires penned behind the grey estuarine clays of coastal salt marshes, and substantial thicknesses of peat are recorded – for example, inland peat deposits near Glastonbury and Queen's Sedgemoor are up to 5 metres thick.

The youngest sediments on the Somerset Wetlands are still being formed today. When in flood the present rivers and streams which drain across the wetlands are spreading a veneer of alluvial muds and silts seawards over all the older sediments and rocks.

The message from the Somerset Wetland's geological history and ancient past is that of continuing changes between terrestrial 'expansion' and marine 'invasion'. Today's predictions of global warming and rising sea levels suggest that another phase of this ever-changing process is underway. Certainly climate change and endangered species are not new phenomena – the Somerset Wetlands have seen it all before, time and time again!

Landscape and Vegetation Change in the Somerset Moors from about 8000BC

Vanessa Straker

The vegetation of the Somerset Moors over the last 10 000 years or so owes its character to geology and geomorphology, climate, sea level changes, drainage patterns and human interaction with the landscape.

The Somerset moors have formed in a broad sediment-filled valley or inlet, up to 30 m deep in places, which drains north westwards into the main valley of the Severn Estuary. The present-day rivers Parrett, Brue, Axe and Huntspill flow into the Severn through this area. The Brue and Axe valleys are confined between the Mendip upland to the north, composed largely of Carboniferous limestone, and the Lias limestone of the Polden Hills to the south. A smaller Lias limestone outcrop, the Wedmore ridge, separates the Brue and Axe valleys. The Parrett and its tributary, the Cary, flow largely between the Polden Hills and the Devonian sandstones and slates of the Quantock Hills. As well as isolated Lias outcrops such as at Godney, Westhay and Meare, there were areas of sands and gravels known as the Burtle Beds. These are thought to date from the Ipswichian interglacial (about 135,000–110,000 years ago) and would have also formed 'islands' in salt marsh or freshwater wetland. The largely base-rich geology, from which water runs off into the Moors, has helped influence the character of the early vegetation.

The valley system filled up with silty and sandy clays and peats in the Holocene (from about 10,000 years ago to the present). The character of the deposits is largely the result of climate warming and sea level change, since the end of the last Ice Age. At its coldest stage (termed glacial maximum) at around 24,000–18,000 years ago, mean sea level was in the order of 130–140m lower than present levels. Mean annual temperature in the area rose by approximately 15°C between the glacial maximum and the onset

Intertidal mud flat with peat beds at Burnham-on-Sea.

of the Holocene about 10,500 years ago. The principal effect of the climatic warming was the release of glacial meltwater causing sea levels to rise. The result was that the sea started to re enter the Bristol Channel and Severn Estuary around 11 000 years ago. The initial rise was very rapid, such that most was accomplished by around 6000 years ago, roughly coincident with the later Mesolithic – early Neolithic periods. Understanding the nature of past sea level has to take account of a complex inter-action of regional and local factors. One such is the effect of compacting peat under several metres of clay, as S Haslett and colleagues demonstrated at the base of Nyland Hill in the Axe Valley. Here, the present height of the peat is over 2 m lower than when it formed. It is thus at a different altitude from peats of a similar age elsewhere in the Somerset moors that have not suffered similar compaction. This means that the altitude of peat to clay transitions cannot necessarily be taken as a guide to past sea level.

There were considerable variations in wetland vegetation development in the different parts of the Somerset Moors. As the vegetation was related to changing estuarine and freshwater conditions, it may be helpful to summarise the sequence of sediments filling the main valley. While sediments in the coastal Levels are similar to the general sequence for the Severn Estuary, the inland Moors differ in some respects.

The earliest (lowest) fills were studied from boreholes in the coastal area. The earliest dated deposits are from wood fen peat in deep channels (to about 20 m below OD) at Highbridge. These peats formed between about 7900 and 7000 BC. Younger peat beds dating from around 5000-4000 BC, can be seen at low tide at Burnham-on-sea and Brean Down. Tree stumps, remnants of oak fen woodland that grew during episodes free from marine flooding, are visible at Stolford.

In the central Brue valley, coring on Shapwick Heath shows up to 7 m of sediments, with laminated muds and tufas (calcium carbonate precipitate) and Lias gravel at the base, assumed to date to the earlier Holocene. These are overlain by a very compacted lower peat which started to form some-time between 5720-5530 BC. This was then flooded by estuarine waters resulting in the deposition of silty clays about 2.8 m in thickness. This flooding was very widespread and extended inland round Glastonbury, as far as Queen's Sedgemoor and Street and northwards, to the foot of the Mendips to the north east of Godney.

Old peat digging on Westhay Level showing peat on estuarine clay.

Sometime around 4600-4200 BC, a change from estuarine silts to largely freshwater peat is visible, as a result of reduced flooding of tidal waters. The age range given above is based on a variety of radio carbon dates for the peat/clay junction, at several places in the central Brue valley. This major change was caused by several possible factors. These include a slow down in the rate of sea level rise, a fall in relative sea level, protection of inland areas from the sea by coastal dunes or other barriers, or a combi-nation of some of these. In the central Brue valley, these peats were never subsequently flooded by estuarine water and continued to develop in places both north and south of the Polden Hills until the medieval period or later. However, towards the coast, the more typical Severn Estuary sequence is seen, where peat and silt bands are buried by estuarine silt (alluvium) by the later Bronze Age or before and do not re-establish. A rare exception is a late Bronze Age to Early Iron Age (about 900-500 BC) salt marsh peat exposed near Withybridge Farm on the Huntspill River.

Intertidal peat bed at Burnham-on-Sea.

Estuarine alluvium also penetrated through the Bleadney-Panborough gap from the Axe valley, reaching to between Godney Island and the north west of Glastonbury. Here as on the coast, the inundation is dated from the late 2nd to mid 1st millennium BC, that is, the late Bronze Age to early Iron Age.

GR

Reed Mace, *Typha latifolia* shedding fruits.

The sediment sequence on Sedgemoor is less well studied, mainly because there has been less peat cutting. In general, sediments are up to 4-6 m deep, and are mainly peats resting on an estuarine silty clay base. There is a shallow capping of silty clay over the peat in some places.

Our understanding of vegetation development and change over the last 8 000 years, summarised below, draws upon the published and unpublished work of the many people mentioned in the acknowledgements. The first to draw attention to the potential of the area and provide the basic vegetation sequence was Sir Harry Godwin in the 1940s. He studied wooden structures exposed in peat cuttings and their environmental context. He was a pioneer in the use of pollen analysis and laid the foundations for the many later studies.

The lower peats and silts have largely remained wet and anaerobic and because of this preserve pollen grains, fragile insect and other arthropod remains and delicate plant macrofossils (fruits, seeds, wood, buds etc) which do not survive in drier, more biologically active conditions. These allow us to identify the different types of vegetation which colonised the Somerset Moors in the past. Remains of insects, fruits, seeds, leaves, buds and rhizomes give more precise detail of local conditions than is possible with pollen, particularly with respect to the immediate environment through which the prehistoric wooden trackways ran. Pollen and spores are airborne and so also tell us about the changing vegetation on the surrounding dry land. Sea level studies and understanding of the conditions that led to the deposition of the silty clays, rely largely on the survival of diatoms (single-celled algae) and foraminifera (protozoans).

Much of the early work was on sites in the Brue Valley, the result of the discovery of trackways during peat cutting. In the last 15 years or so studies have focussed more widely in the Moors such as, for example, peat up to 5m in depth on the outskirts of Glastonbury and on Queen's Sedgemoor. Recent research in the coastal area at Pawlett near Bridgwater, along the banks of the Huntspill and in the intertidal zone at Burnham-on-Sea follows from the early studies of Kidson and Heyworth. It has greatly improved our understanding of the lower sediments in the valley, the vegetation they supported and insight into the western part of the Somerset Levels and Moors.

In the central Brue valley there are few studies of the earliest vegetation and we rely on information from the southern end of Shapwick Heath, close to the Polden Hills where the sediments are about 7 m deep. The base of the lowest peat at the bottom of the valley-fill dates to 5720-5530 BC. The

GR

Typha latifolia.

peat-forming vegetation was wet woodland, mainly alder carr with some birch, willow, hazel and oak, but there were also open water and swamp habitats supporting plants such as common reed, bur-reeds, sedges and bulrushes. The alder declined somewhat before estuarine flooding deposited silty clays, as conditions probably became too brackish, before the peat stopped forming, for alder to continue to grow. This early period of wet woodland and swamp may only have lasted for a few hundred years.

The subsequent environment was a late Mesolithic salt marsh (characterised by the silty clays), which, as noted above, was very extensive, reaching as far inland as Glastonbury. Salt marsh vegetation varies depending upon its position in the tidal frame; this is controlled by the extent of inundation and exposure during the tidal cycle. Mud flats are largely unvegetated and are exposed for a short time, whereas high salt marsh can be drained of sea water and exposed for several hours per tide. Thus, salt marshes comprise mud flats, creeks, tidal rivers (visible today as palaeochannels) and vegetation of different types depending on the degree of inundation they experience. Prehistoric salt marsh deposits have been studied in most detail on the Pawlett Level (see below).

Between around 4600-4200 BC, in the last few hundred years of the Mesolithic period, before the farming communities became established on the higher ground in and surrounding the Moors, the great salt marsh receded. Freshwater conditions, shown by renewed peat accumulation (the upper peat), became established once again.

The general vegetation sequence from the base of the upper peat is a classic hydroseral succession and is summarised from the base upwards as follows:

- Bulrushes *Typha sp.* are early colonisers of the clays with Common Reed *Phragmites communis*. *Phragmites* reedswamp (fen) communities became established, with some shallowing of the water suggested by Great Fen-sedge *Cladium mariscus* growth, suggesting base-rich water conditions. The eutrophic (nutrient rich) nature of the water through which the Sweet Track ran, is demonstrated by the presence in the fen peats of three species of beetle, *Chlaenius sulcicollis*, *C. tristis* and *Oodes gracilis*, which are extinct in the British Isles today.

- Above this, when peat growth raised the bog surface high enough for better drainage, or the groundwater levels dropped slightly, fen carr developed, with dominance of alder, birch or willow varying locally, development starting at different times in different places. The Sweet Track (3807-3806 BC) lies mainly below the fenwood, in the reedswamp peat. By around 3500 BC in the early Neolithic period, the growth of fen carr had replaced reedswamp in many areas.

● Over much of the central Brue valley, but excluding the Glastonbury area, as peat growth further raised the bog surface above the largely calcareous groundwater, nutrient levels fell and the fen carr peat was succeeded by the development of raised bog. This acid-loving vegetation did not rely on high ground water and was fed by rainfall. Raised bogs are typically slightly domed and consist of drier hummocks supporting plants such as Cross-leaved Heath *Erica tetralix,* Ling *Calluna vulgaris*, Hare's-tail Cotton Grass *Eriophorum vaginatum* and Bog Myrtle *Myrica gale*. Raised bog also includes wetter pools with *Sphagnum* moss and shallow water aquatics such as Bog Bean *Menyanthes trifoliata*. There were some episodes of freshwater flooding, one dated to around 1000 BC, enabling great fen sedge communities to re-establish for a time. At some sites, however, the hydroseral succession is from *Cladium* and fen-moss dominated vegetation, to acid fen with species such as bog mosses *Sphagnum* species, White Beak-sedge *Rhyncospora alba* and Cotton Grass.

● Around the margins of the raised bog and the higher ground, there would have been a very wet area (lagg) with base-rich water accumulated from run-off from the higher ground and some water-shed from the bog surface. Here, alder/willow carr woodland with open water pools continued to grow.

Detailed botanical and insect studies throughout the Somerset Moors have shown that there are many variations to this general picture, with local growth of birch carr or wet acid fen in some areas before the raised bog started to grow. There were several centres for raised bog development. In some areas, flooding of the raised bog is indicated by the return of shallow base-rich *Cladium* fen. These flooding horizons vary from place to place and, as far as present evidence suggests, are most pronounced on Meare Heath where three possible returns to wetter conditions are suggested by the insects and pollen. The flooding horizons may well be the indirect result of an increase in the rate of sea level rise. But, increased tree clearance and human pressure on the surrounding dry land may have led to increased freshwater runoff acting as a contributory factor.

Around Glastonbury, raised bog did not succeed alder carr woodland. The shallow lake mud

Sphagnum moss.

VS

K. CRABTREE

Far left: Reedswamp with *Phragmites communis.*

Left: Raised bog (SW Ireland).

VS
GR

Above: Hare's-tail Cotton Grass *Eriophorum vaginatum.*

Right: *Sphagnum* moss.

34

supported aquatics such as pondweeds *Potamogeton* and *Ceratophyllum* through to alder and willow fen carr with some oak. The oak trunks survive today as 'bog oaks' in peat.

To the north west on Godney Moor, after a short-lived episode of birch carr, reed swamp and sedge fen established due to high levels of freshwater. These open wetlands would have included Common Reed, sedges *Carex* species and Great Fen-sedge *Cladium mariscus*, cotton grass and many aquatic herbaceous species.

At the same time that changes were taking place on the wetland, the mixed deciduous woodland that had developed on the higher ground also changed. The woodland included trees such as oak, elm, lime, hazel, birch, alder, holly and willow. Some temporary clearance of elm and later lime is evident, when the fenwood grew in the wetlands, but by about 3100 BC, when raised bog had developed on much of the central Brue Valley, forest regeneration had occurred. The pollen diagrams chart further forest clearance and regeneration on the dry land during the later Bronze Age (from about 1200 BC) and in much of the 1st millennium BC there is increased evidence for woodland clearance and cultivation.

Much of Sedgemoor seems to have been affected by very high ground water and been very wet throughout most of its history. This may have made it less attractive for settlement, though no doubt it was valuable for wildfowling and fishing. An environmental survey of Sedgemoor carried out in 1982 identified a diversity of past wetland environments and some sediment inwash from tree clearance on the Polden Hills.

At Greylake on King's Sedgemoor, some time around 2000 BC, fen with alder carr was established before higher ground water led to the development of base-rich *Cladium* fen, which tolerates up to 0.4m of standing water. This was presenting in much of the area and is particularly noticeable in the late Bronze Age (1300-1000 BC) when flooding horizons are seen in many parts of the Somerset Moors. Such were the conditions when a late Bronze Age timber structure at Greylake was in use. Fresh water pond snails and seeds of plants, such as Yellow and White Water Lilies *Nuphar* and *Nymphaea,* also identify some substantial areas of nutrient-rich open water.

Despite the very wet conditions in much of the area, raised bog did develop in the central part of North Moor.

Round-leaved Sundew *Drosera rotundifolia*

Round-leaved Sundew on Greater Westhay reserve. The leaves bear many red hairs each tipped with a sticky fluid which traps small insects. These are digested to gain essential nutrients. This is an adaptation to living on acid heaths and moors where such nutrients have been leached away.

Derek Briggs

As noted above, we now have a much better knowledge of the nature of the early prehistoric vegetation in the outer Brue valley (the present coastal belt), thanks to work carried out in advance of the construction of the Walpole landfill site near Pawlett and from the excavation of a saltern near East Huntspill.

Estuarine clays, organic clays (including a late Neolithic buried soil) and peats accumulated around a now invisible Lias outcrop which would have been exposed as an island in prehistory, probably until some time in the Roman period or shortly after it. The sequence investigated accumulated over some 5000 years from about 4700 BC and demonstrates a varied local environment including woodland, freshwater marsh and salt marsh. The late Mesolithic (about 4800–4200) was a relatively dry period of salt marsh emergence associated with a slow down in the rate of sea level rise or reduced marine influence, possibly coupled with a temporary coastal barrier. The salt marsh was colonised by Chenopodiaceae (Sea Blite, glasswort, oraches or Sea Beet) which alternated with reed or other grass-dominated communities as water tables fluctuated around the island. There was also freshwater seepage from the dry land, allowing freshwater communities to flourish around spring flushes or small streams. The steeply sloping margins around the bedrock island resulted in a sharp transition between dryland and marsh and restricted the development of upper salt marsh. This compares with a series of mud flat/lower salt marsh and upper salt marsh communities succeeded by reedswamp with wet birch/willow woodland in the vicinity, which grew between about 5500 BC and about 3370 BC in a more gently shelving situation, on what is now the beach at Burnham-on-Sea.

At Pawlett, the pollen shows that the dry land vegetation on the higher ground was oak-hazel woodland, with a little elm, lime and ash throughout the time the salt marsh deposits were accumulating. Woodland similar to this existed on the Lias island, Pawlett Burtle, and probably also Brent Knoll. Other studies show that broadly similar woods also existed on the dry land around Woolavington Bridge and further inland in the Ham Walls area and on the Polden Hills. Small scale clearances followed by regeneration were identified in the Pawlett peats. Late Mesolithic burning of the reed swamps is evident on the Pawlett Levels, Ham Walls and in the Woolavington Bridge area, possibly to aid hunting by flushing out wildfowl and encouraging large herbivores to eat new growth. The fine charcoal lenses in the sediments could also result from the fires of temporary camps of wildfowlers and hunters on the higher ground.

Opposite page:
Roosting cormorants in
flooded wetland. LN

PHC

Flower-rich meadow.

By about 4350-4040 cal BC salt marshes were some distance to the west of Woolavington Bridge, though there may have been occasional incursions of brackish water at high tides. Here the reed bed community was succeeded by birch fen woodland, and ultimately by raised bog. Despite the fact that from the late-Mesolithic until the post-Roman periods the area was colonised by fresh water vegetation, salt marshes and tidal influence were not far to the east.

There is an established view that peat stopped forming in the Somerset peat moors around 400 AD. However, we now have firm evidence, from several radiocarbon dates in the Brue Valley (Godney Moor and Glastonbury area) and on Sedgemoor (West Sedgemoor and North Moor), that peat continued to grow well into the medieval period and indeed at one location on West Sedgemoor, possibly until the time of the Parliamentary enclosures. The lack of recent peat survival in other areas is likely to be due to one or more of several possibilities. Foremost amongst these are centuries of peat cutting for fuel, peat cutting for horticulture and peat wastage (shrinkage and erosion) as a result of drainage to aid ground improvement for arable and pasture. Early drainage and reclamation may also have slowed or halted peat growth in some areas, with flooding only on a seasonal rather than permanent basis.

The flower-rich hay meadows within the Shapwick Heath National Nature Reserve, which are managed in the traditional manner, provide a glimpse of how some of the grassland looked in the past. The charred remains of wetland plants such as Great Fen-sedge and spike rushes *Eleocharis* spp., found on the various Roman and Medieval excavations in Shapwick, are likely to have come from plants grown on the nearby Moors, either in peat for fuel or collected for use as thatch or for strewing on floors.

Dunning in this book describes the uses of the Levels and Moors, their importance for pasture in the Medieval period and the major drainage operations which started in the 12th century, under the auspices of Glastonbury Abbey and other major land owners.

The discussion above illustrates the complexity of the changing wetland environments of the Somerset Levels and Moors, with a diversity of habitats changing over time in relation to a range of natural factors, and particularly in the last 2000 years, the activities of its inhabitants.

Note: All date ranges quoted are calibrated 2 sigma (95% confidence) ranges of radiocarbon dates.

A Window on the Past – The prehistoric archaeology of the Somerset Moors

Richard Brunning

Trying to understand the prehistoric period is like trying to do a jigsaw when you can't see the picture and you only have 5% of the pieces. This is because the vast majority of everyday items and structures of those times were made of organic materials, such as wood, that do not normally survive. The deep peat deposits of the Avalon Marshes, west of Glastonbury, are special; for thousands of years they have preserved a much more complete picture of past societies as their waterlogged condition has kept out the oxygen that allows bacterial and fungal decay of organic remains. If you read on you will discover what the prehistoric story is like when you have half the jigsaw.

In the Brue valley layers of peat up to 6 metres thick have formed over many millennia and have been cut away by man since Roman times. Over the last 200 years numerous exciting archaeological discoveries have been made by peat cutters. The Rev William Stradling who recorded the finding of flint and bronze axes, pottery, and wooden bowls, paddles and prehistoric canoes noted the first of these in the early 19th century.

The first trackway to be discovered was a corduroy road made of alder logs that linked the islands of Burtle and Westhay. When it was found in 1873 it was named the 'Abbot's Way' as it was thought to have been made on the orders of the Abbot of Glastonbury who had owned the land in the medieval period. In fact the trackway was built four and a half thousand years ago, over 3,000 years before the first Abbot of Glastonbury was born.

A. Forrestier

Detailed records of the trackways were first made by C W Dymond, a Fellow of the Society of Antiquaries, who excavated part of the Abbot's Way in 1873, and later by Arthur Bulleid, a local amateur archaeologist who later rose to fame as the excavator of the lake villages (see below). In the mid 20th century Sir Harry Godwin, then Professor of Botany at Cambridge, worked in the valley, establishing the basic environmental sequence and excavating structures uncovered in the peat cuttings. He was assisted by Stephen Dewar, an amateur archaeologist who lived close by on the Polden ridge, who maintained very close links with the peat-cutters, a relationship lubricated by occasional gifts of an alcoholic variety.

Most of the 43 groups of wooden trackways were excavated in advance of their destruction by peat cutting in the 1970's and 1980's by the Somerset Levels Project, directed by John and Bryony Coles. They pioneered many of the techniques of wetland archaeology that are still in use around the world today.

SOMERSET LEVELS PROJECT

The Neolithic Abbot's Way.

Often structures and artefacts were found and reported by the peat cutters themselves and many of the trackways were named after their discoverer or the peat company or farmer who owned the land, such as the Eclipse, Tinney's, Baker, Garvin's and Rowland's tracks. The most famous of the trackways was the Sweet Track that crossed the 2km of reedswamp that separated the island of Westhay from the dryland of the Polden ridge to the south. It was named after Ray Sweet who discovered it while ditch cleaning.

The wood used in the Sweet Track provides evidence of what the untouched primary forest was like before any trees were felled. It consisted of a mix of oak, lime, ash and hazel dominated by huge oak trees up to 400 years old, over a metre across, and with trunks as high as 20m above ground before the first branch. Such high canopy forest has disappeared from almost all of Europe now, but its character can be glimpsed in the hunting forests of eastern Poland.

Tree-ring dating (dendrochronology) has proved that the Sweet Track was built in the spring of 3806 BC when farming and settled life was just beginning in what is called the 'Neolithic' period. The forests were beginning to be cleared to create areas for domesticated animals and arable crops, although wild food was still an important part of the diet. Fats extracted from pottery found beside the track were from cow's milk, providing the earliest evidence of dairy farming in the UK.

An even earlier trackway, called the Post Track, was built on the same line as the Sweet Track in 3838 BC and is the oldest trackway known from the UK. It may have lasted the 32 years until the Sweet Track was built, but repairs were only made to the latter for less than 10 years, after which it seems to have been abandoned.

The dry woodland was also managed, with large areas of hazel trees being coppiced in both the Neolithic and the subsequent Bronze Age. In this system the trees were felled at ground level in order to stimulate the growth of numerous shoots and over a few years these produced long straight stems that were perfect for making woven hurdles for fencing, or as panels to form trackways across the raised bog.

Other simpler tracks were made of dumps of brushwood laid along the line of the route and pegged in place by small stakes. These were the most common form of trackway built to cross the bog. In the later Bronze Age, between 1400BC and 800BC, the raised bog surface became much wetter, possibly as a result of climate change, and more substantial trackways had to be built. The most impressive of these was the Meare Heath Track that was made from large oak planks laid on top of dumps of brushwood and tranverse planks that operated like railway sleepers.

To prehistoric people the wetlands of the Avalon Marshes were not just an inconvenience that had to be crossed. They were also an important source of food in the form of fish, wildfowl and mammals such as Otter and Beaver, which also provided fur. The reeds could be used as roofing material and the fen woodland was exploited for fuel, building material, the manufacture of rope, string and birch bark tar (for use as an adhesive) and herbal medicines, such as willow bark for pain relief.

The wetlands had a central role in prehistoric religious beliefs. Numerous Neolithic and Bronze Age artefacts have been found in the peat, either as stray finds or beside trackways. Some of these may be the result of accidental loss, such as broken pots full of hazelnuts, but most were probably deliberately deposited as offerings to the gods of the wetlands, such as the hoard of bronze axes discovered near Edington Burtle. Some of these offerings included what were probably the most valuable possessions of those cultures, such as a polished jadeite axe that had come all the way from the French Alps but had never been used or even hafted before it was deposited beside the Sweet Track.

The offerings were usually made in areas of shallow water where they might still be visible for a time before disappearing under the growing peat. At Greylake, just to the south of the Polden hills, an area of shallow freshwater fen was marked out by a series of oak posts in 963 BC and additional timbers were added over at least the next eleven years. Defleshed human bones were scattered in

Dr Bryony Coles standing beside an excavated stretch of the Sweet Track.

this area – possibly after excarnation (exposure of the body) on a platform on the nearby dry land; sheep bones and broken pottery suggest an associated feast took place. A bronze axe had been deposited after being deliberately broken, or 'killed', possibly so that it could accompany its owner into the next life.

Sometimes large structures were made for ritual purposes. At Harter's Hill on Queen's Sedgemoor the Harding Alignment, named after its discoverer, was built at least 100m out into a shallow fen in 1076 BC. It consisted of two to three rows of large oak posts surrounded by a mass of worked wood. A structure of similar date and construction near Peterborough called Flag Fen is known to be associated with ritual offerings in the wetlands - the same was probably happening at Harter's Hill where a bronze sword was found in the early 20th century.

In the Iron Age period the Brue valley was much wetter than before and dugout canoes replaced trackways as the main method of traversing the wetlands. The first reported canoe find, was made by the Reverend W. Stradling in the early 19th century when much of the Iron age peat was being cut for fuel:

I have to lament the loss of a most interesting relic. It was a very large canoe, and was formed from an immense oak. I understand it was long known as 'Squire Phippen's big ship' and it made its appearance partially in very dry seasons. I met with this information too late, and to my great mortification, I one day had a piece of the poor old 'ship' brought to me, and was told she had been broken up in the dry weather, and used by the cottagers for fuel. The oak was as firm as when the vessel was sunk perhaps 2000 years since, the peat in which it was discovered having such a wonderfully preservative power.

Four other canoes have been found in the Avalon Marshes, one in the foundations of Glastonbury lake village, one near Godney (now on display in Glastonbury Tribunal), another from the old vicarage garden at Meare and one found at Shapwick Station in 1906 half way between Shapwick and Meare. The Shapwick canoe can be seen in the County Museum, Taunton Castle, but a replica of it can be seen at the Peat Moors Centre.

In 1892 a young medical student from Glastonbury discovered an archaeological site on the nearby peat moors that was destined to become one of the most famous Iron Age sites in Europe. His name was Arthur Bulleid and he had recently read about the discoveries of prehistoric lake dwellings uncovered in Switzerland. Living beside a large area of wetland, Bulleid, an amateur antiquarian, thought that similar remains might exist in Somerset and spent four years looking for them until, in March 1982, he noticed

SOMERSET LEVELS PROJECT

The late Bronze Age
Mear Heath track.

SOMERSET COUNTY MUSEUM SERVICE

SOMERSET LEVELS PROJECT

SOMERSET COUNTY MUSEUM SERVICE

Top left: The Edington Burtle hoard.

Top right: The Neolithic
Walton Heath hurdle tracks.

Left: The Shapwick canoe in 1906.

43

a field covered in small mounds. Brief excavation showed that there were well preserved roundhouses with a varied array of everyday items of the late Iron Age.

What Arthur Bulleid had discovered was the best preserved prehistoric village ever found in the United Kingdom, ranking alongside the great monuments of Avebury and Stonehenge in its archaeological importance. Bulleid began an excavation at what soon became known as 'Glastonbury lake-village' in 1892 and carried on until 1898 and then again between 1904 and 1907 in company with Harold St George Gray, the curator of the Somerset Archaeology and Natural History Museum in Taunton. The excavations were funded by donations from visitors and funds from the Glastonbury Antiquarian Society to whom Edward Bath donated the field and who owns it still.

The settlement that Bullied and Gray excavated had not been built in a lake as the name suggests, but was in fact created at the edge of a patch of birch, alder and willow trees, in the midst of a large swamp of reed, sedge, open water and wet woodland that stretched all the way to Glastonbury. Through numerous channels in this swamp the sluggish waters of the River Brue slowly headed north towards the Axe valley.

To build a settlement in such a wetland required a large amount of effort as Bulleid discovered:

On the surface of the peat is a layer or platform of timber and brushwood kept in place by numerous small piles at the margin. On this a layer of clay is placed, slightly raised at the centre, where the remains of a hearth are generally found. The dwelling itself was composed of timber filled in with wattle and daub. Not only have the wall-posts been found in situ, but also the entrance threshold and doorstep.

About 40 such roundhouses, 5 to 8 metres in diameter, were built during the life of the settlement, with probably a maximum of 14 at any one time in the village's habitation between about 250 and 50 BC. The enormous effort required to build and maintain a settlement in such a wet environment begs the question 'why there?' There is no definitive answer but it may have been because of the protection offered by the encompassing swamp or the importance of the fish and birds that lived in it. The site may have been located on an important water borne trade route from central Somerset to the Severn estuary. A dugout canoe, made from a hollowed out tree trunk, was found in the foundations and another one in a nearby field. Canoes may have landed at a causeway that was built on one side of the village.

SOMERSET COUNTY MUSEUM SERVICE

Arthur Bulleid (left) and
St George Gray (right).

Remains of bones and plants show that the villagers were eating a wide variety of food from both wild and domesticated species. The wetlands surrounding the settlement yielded perch, roach, trout, eels, frogs, numerous types of duck, pelicans, cranes, swans, herons, bitterns, otters and beavers as well as numerous edible plants. Lead sinkers for nets and baked clay sling shots show how these animals were caught. Dry land animals were also eaten, sheep being the most numerous of the domesticated animals with some cattle, pig, horse and dog. Wheat, barley, beans and peas were also present, possibly acquired in exchange for fish or wildfowl. Roe and red deer, wild boar, fox and wildcat were caught in the dry woodlands while the presence of Puffin, Cormorant and Sea Eagle suggest contact with the coast.

The range of everyday items of Iron Age life discovered at the village is staggering. In addition to vast amounts of plain and decorated pots of varying sizes, the waterlogged nature of the peat preserved wooden items for several thousand years. Thus the tools such as billhooks, saws and chisels still retain their handles and wooden objects such as a ladle, a chopping board, a ladder, parts of a wheel and a wooden frame for stretching skins have been found. There were also woven baskets, carved and lathe-turned bowls, stave built buckets and rectangular boxes made by steaming and bending wood into shape.

Personal ornaments included bronze and iron brooches, pins and rings, shale armlets, glass beads, a pair of tweezers and a bronze mirror. Spindle whorls and loom weights show that cloth was made in the village and the numerous small combs found were used to make braids or other narrow strips of material. Metal, especially bronze, was worked on site and a beautiful sheet bronze bowl was discovered. An antler shaker and a set of bar shaped dice that had dots representing the numbers three to six were found, suggesting that gaming may have been taking place.

At its height, about 200 people in 14 roundhouses would have occupied the settlement. Very little trace survives of the inhabitants themselves. The burials of ten newly born infants were found in the village, but the last resting place of the other villagers was elsewhere, possibly beneath the waters of the swamp in a sacred spot, or cremated, with the ashes scattered across the water. Four complete skulls and many skull fragments were found, mostly close to the palisade. The complete skulls bore cut marks caused by sword blows that had probably been the cause of death. These unfortunates, who included at least one woman, may have been enemies of the villagers, killed in tribal warfare.

For Bulleid and Gray the work on lake villages did not stop at Glastonbury, for the find of some pottery in a peat field just north of the village of Meare led to the discovery of two more lake villages, 'Meare

The Glastonbury bowl.

The Neolithic 'God Dolly', a wooden figurine with both male and female characteristics, found under the Bell Track.

Canoes landing at Glastonbury lake village. by A. Forrestier.

Glastonbury lake village at its greatest extent.

East and West'. Bulleid and Gray excavated there from 1909 until 1956 but, unlike Glastonbury, a large proportion of the settlement was never disturbed, although there were some smaller excavations in the 1960s and by the Somerset Levels Project in the 1980s.

The Meare Lake Villages were built on a drying part of the raised bog just 100m north of Meare island and were bordered on their northern side by a large wet fen and open water that seasonally flooded the area of the settlements. Although there is considerable evidence of floors made of clay and wood with central hearths, only five examples appear to have been in roundhouses. Other posts formed simple lines like wind breaks and it appears that most of the area was occupied by either tents or open working spaces. There is considerable evidence for craft activities such as spinning, weaving, making artefacts of bone, antler and shale, beads of glass and objects of iron and bronze. Unlike the permanent settlement at Glastonbury lake village, Meare appears to have functioned as a seasonal market and possibly a meeting place for people from a much wider area.

Taming a Wetland Wilderness – Romano-British and Medieval reclamation in the Somerset Levels and Moors

Stephen Rippon

Wetlands dominate the landscape of Somerset, and the drainage of the Levels and Moors represents a remarkable human achievement. These wetlands are quite rightly valued for their nature conservation interest but they are far from a 'natural' environment: the wide range of freshwater flora and fauna that the Levels and Moors support today are a direct result of a human transformation of this landscape, and the flood defences and drainage systems are very special cultural artefacts. This article is a summary of recent research into the creation of the 'historic landscape': the pattern of fields, roads, settlements and watercourses that we use today, but which in many areas is over a thousand years old.

On the eve of the Roman Conquest, the Somerset Levels were a complex mosaic of wetland environments, with intertidal mudflats and salt-marshes towards the coast being replaced by freshwater reed-swamp and sedge fens further inland. These wetlands offer human communities a range of natural resources that they could exploit, including rich grazing for sheep and cattle, alongside the opportunity for fishing and wildfowling. Sea water could also be gently heated to produce salt, and Late Iron Age salterns have been located at Badgworth near Brent Knoll in the main Somerset Levels, and at several locations on the North Somerset Levels (Banwell Moor, Puxton Dolemoor and West Wick near Weston-super-Mare (in the North Somerset Levels). In the two centuries following the Roman Conquest there was a marked intensification of this salt industry, notably around Burnham,

Autumn sunrise. LN

Highbridge and Huntspill, but in addition to the exploitation of these natural resources, human communities also started to modify their environment to improve its agricultural productivity. On the Puxton Dolemoors, for example, a ditched enclosure system dating to the 1st/2nd centuries was dug on the surface of a high intertidal salt-marsh, and was used for grazing livestock.

Nigel Cameron, Paul Davies, Julie Jones, Annette Kreiser and Heather Tinsley, have looked at the well-preserved palaeo-environmental material (the waterlogged plant and animal remains) from several of the ditches. They report that the herbaceous pollen from the basal fill is characterised by high frequencies of Chenopodiaceae (10-20% TLP) and values of this order are normally interpreted as originating from salt-marsh communities. The Chenopodiaceae family includes many halophytic taxa such as Sea Blite *Suaeda maritima*, glassworts *Salicornia* spp, and oraches *Atriplex* spp. and with other pollen taxa such as *Solidago virgaurea*-type (which includes Daisy and Sea Aster, as well as a range of other related Asteraceae), suggesting that the source of the pollen is likely to have been from upper salt-marsh communities growing on tidal flats very close to the ditched enclosure system. The local vegetation immediately around the ditch appears to have been a somewhat disturbed community of grasses (Poaceae – grasses, forming 11-23% TLP) with Ribwort Plantain *Plantago lanceolata* and

Palaeo-environmental sampling of an early Romano-British ditch at Puxton Dolemoor. The water-logged conditions have ensured excellent preservation of plant remains including pollen, along with diatoms and foraminifera, that together suggest that this field system was dug on the surface of a high intertidal salt-marsh.

Aerial photograph of the relict landscape at Kenn Moor, the earthworks of which can be seen on the left. A series of carefully targeted small-scale excavations in the fields at the bottom and on the right provided a range of palaeo-environment assemblages that show that, unlike the intertidal setting of the earlier enclosure system at Puxton Dolemoor, the late Roman landscape on the North Somerset Levels was freshwater and therefore reclaimed.

mugwort *Artemisia* sp. Occasional pollen grains of pondweed *Potamogeton* sp. indicate the presence of some freshwater in the ditch system even in this early stage of reclamation from salt-marsh. Diatoms suggest tidal conditions with marine species comprising almost 50% of the assemblage, with over 35% brackish water and almost 10% marine-brackish taxa. Freshwater and even brackish-freshwater diatoms are absent. Foraminifera preservation was poor with only a few tests of agglutinated forms from vegetated high or middle marsh habitats. Somerset was not alone in seeing such improvement being made to the drainage on intertidal marshes: very similar ditched enclosure systems have recently been recorded further up the Severn Estuary at Avonmouth, and across the Estuary on the Caldicot Level.

These localised drainage systems would have improved the agricultural productivity to a certain extent, but the landscape was still prone to flooding. Around the 3rd century AD, however, the communities living on and around the Somerset Levels embarked on a major transformation of their wetland, through constructing a set of embankments along the coast (where it was not protected by sand dunes) and along the major tidal rivers. None of these embankments has survived an episode of late/post-Roman coastal erosion and flooding but the evidence for this Romano-British reclamation is widespread, albeit usually buried under later alluvium.

On Banwell Moor and Kenn Moor in North Somerset a series of extensive field systems were laid out, and unlike their early Roman counterparts on Puxton Moor, these ditches contained a range of wholly freshwater habitats directly comparable to the field boundary ditches and rhynes in today's landscape. At Puxton Dolemoor the old ditched enclosure system was left to silt up and the change to a freshwater, reclaimed environment is reflected by its colonisation by bur reeds *Sparganium* spp. and/or Lesser Bulrush *Typha angustifolia*, Common Club-rush *Schoenoplectus lacustris*, with herbaceous taxa such as Tubular Water-dropwort *Oenanthe fistulosa*, Water Mint *Mentha aquatica*, Gipsywort *Lycopus europaeus* and Celery-leaved Buttercup *Ranunculus sceleratus*. Within the ditch itself, spores of *Spirogyra* and *Mougeotia* (an alga of the family Zygnemataceae) suggest the development of algal mats, while much of the water's surface would have been covered by duckweed and Rigid Hornwort *Ceratophyllum demersum*, both taxa suggesting still water conditions. Taxa like Water Plantain *Alisma plantago-aquatica* and Mare's-tail *Hippuris vulgaris* also point to a predominantly freshwater environment. Occasional leech cocoons, caddis fly larvae and statoblasts of *Lophopus crystallinus*, freshwater bryozoans often found adhering to stems of water plants and duckweed fronds, also indicate freshwater conditions.

Celery-leaved Buttercup
Ranunculus sceleratus.

49

SALT, SILVER AND THE SEA – THE BRUE VALLEY IN THE ROMAN PERIOD

After the Roman conquest of Somerset the first attempts at reclaiming the wetlands for agriculture were made. Natural or man made sea defences existed along the Severn estuary as far down as Brent Knoll and traces of Roman settlements, including a villa have been found on the lowlands between the sea and the Wedmore ridge. In the Axe valley aerial photographs show low earthworks that are the remains of extensive field systems, droveways, canals and settlements that would only have been possible if the river had been embanked by flood defences at this time.

In the Brue valley however, there is no evidence of flood defence and reclamation – on the moors north of the Polden ridge the raised bog was still growing. One reason for the difference between the areas may be related to the dozens of low mounds that pepper the landscape of the moors west of Burtle. Local opinion was divided on their function as the Reverend Stradling recorded in 1849:

Often pointed out to me were a number of mounds or barrows, as they were considered by many. They were of various sizes, many of them containing several hundreds loads of the fragments of Roman pottery. Antiquarians were greatly divided in opinion as to the origin or uses of these earthworks. Some thought they contained the bones of the illustrious dead; others that they were heaps of ballast thrown from ships, when the bog formed the bottom of the immense lake; others thought they were rubbish from the numerous Roman buildings in the neighbourhood

In fact the mounds were the result of a huge Roman industry at the western end of the Brue valley, the production of salt from sea water. Excavations have shown how the process took place at the edge of a large salt marsh. Firstly sea water from tidal channels was fed into large circular tanks at high tide, where the sediment in the water settled to the bottom. Then the clear brine was taken out and poured into open lead trays that were raised on clay pedestals over a simple hearth with clay walls and the water gradually evaporated to leave pure salt. The mounds were made of the ashes, sediment from the settling tanks and broken fired clay that were the waste products of the process.

Above: Replica of a saltern hearth in use.
Below: Settling tanks revealed in the Huntspill Cut.

Many hundred Roman saltern sites existed between Burtle and the sea. The clay came from the local marsh, the lead from mines on the Mendip hills and the fuel for the hearths was supplied by peat cut from the raised bog that existed inland of the marsh. The salt itself would have been used for preserving and flavouring food and possibly also in the dyeing industry. It may have been transported away down the tidal creeks to the Severn estuary or inland along the Roman road on the Polden ridge.

The local salt-makers also seem to have had a lucrative sideline. Since 1670 numerous clay moulds for casting Roman silver coins, called denarii, have been found on the moors south-west of Burtle, sometimes associated with the saltern sites. These are evidence of a large counterfeiting operation in the area in the 220s and 230s AD. No doubt the open bog and marsh made it easy to see people coming from a long distance, providing ample time to hide the evidence. Perhaps connected to the salt industry or the counterfeiting, is a hoard of over 9,000 silver denarii found in a villa in Shapwick on the Polden ridge dating to early 230's AD. This is the second largest denarii hoard ever found in the Roman Empire, suggesting that some local was 'coining it in' but didn't live long enough to spend all his wealth.

The salt industry seems to have migrated inland from the coast over several centuries, possibly because of increased erosion of that part of the coast that had no defences. Towards the end of the Roman period in the late 4th century AD the saltern sites were abandoned and became covered with alluvium deposited in a salt marsh that remained in the area for another millennium. Elsewhere the Roman flood and sea defences failed in the face of continuing sea level rise and the fields and settlements on the wetlands were covered by alluvium that hides them from view to this day.

Richard Brunning

This later Romano-British landscape appears to have been used for mixed agriculture, with the cultivation of cereals (wheat and barley) and the grazing of livestock (notably cattle and sheep). The economy at Kenn Moor appears to have been diversified with some metalworking, as was common elsewhere around the Severn Estuary. Most settlements on the Levels appear to have been fairly low-status, perhaps the tenant farms of one of the villas which occur all around the North Somerset Levels at Locking, Banwell, Congresbury, Wraxall, Tickenham and Clevedon. These villas are, however, fairly modest, especially in comparison with that at Wemberham which lies at the very centre of the Levels. Was it the builders of Wemberham who were responsible for reclaiming the North Somerset Levels? South of Mendip, the Brent Marsh area also appears to have been reclaimed as another villa has been identified at Lakehouse Farm, beneath the M5 motorway, along with several substantial stone buildings near Lympsham and Rooksbridge. This reclamation did not, however, extend as far south as the Brue Valley as here salt production continued to flourish, producing the distinctive 'briquetage mounds' that still survive as earthworks around Burtle. Clearly, human communities living in and around the Somerset Levels were making conscious decisions as to whether they could more profitably exploit the rich natural resources of coastal wetlands, or invest in sea defences and drainage systems and improve their agricultural potential.

The Somerset Levels appear to have been abandoned in the later 4th century, possibly due to the declining economy, or possibly due to increased flooding. Large areas were certainly covered in a blanket of estuarine alluvium that seals the villas at Wemberham and Lakehouse Farm, and their associated landscapes. Palaeo-environmental evidence from Banwell Moor, Kenn Moor and Puxton Dolemoor shows that this alluvium was deposited in the context of a range of salt-marshes and mudflats identical to those that were displaced a few centuries earlier: nature had briefly reclaimed the Levels.

By the time of the Domesday survey in 1086 the coastal parts of the Somerset Levels, around Huntspill, Burnham and Brent to the south of Mendip, and around Kingston Seymour in the north, were extensively settled. The date when this occurred is unclear, though it is tempting to see the reclamation of marshland as part of the same process of improving the productivity of the landscape that also saw the reorganisation of dryland landscapes across much of central and south eastern Somerset into villages and open fields. Very little archaeological work has been carried out on this initial phase of the medieval re-colonisation, though at Puxton in North Somerset a programme of archaeological survey, excavation, and palaeo-environmental work has shown that the earliest stage was not the construction of a sea wall

GR

Greater Pond-sedge *Carex riparia*.

along the coast. Instead, the earliest colonisers constructed very broad but low banks around small areas of marsh in order to protect areas of meadow or crops from summer flooding. These oval-shaped enclosures are a common feature on the coastal marshlands of the Somerset Levels, and indeed elsewhere around the Severn Estuary, and at Puxton at least, can be dated to the 10th/11th centuries. These are the earliest parts of today's wetland landscape to have been created, and the fields they enclose still form a functioning part of the historic landscape.

The maintenance of numerous, individual, small reclamations, which would not have been sufficiently substantial to protect the enclosed areas all year round, soon became impractical and at some point the decision was taken to construct more substantial embankments along the open coast and tidal rivers. The numbers of settlements, population and plough teams recorded in Domesday suggests that this process occurred some time before the mid 11th century. Protected by these sturdy embankments, the medieval colonisers set about enclosing and draining the higher, coastal land and by the 13th century most of the alluvial marshes as far east as places like East Huntspill and Mark had been reclaimed and settled. Once again, the best palaeo-environmental evidence for the nature of the flora and fauna living in the watercourses at this time comes from Puxton. The material studied by Nigel Cameron, Paul Davies, Julie Jones, Annette Kreiser and Heather Tinsley reveal a range of freshwater ditch environments exactly the same as those we have today. Aquatic mollusca *Valvata piscinalis* and *Bithynia tentaculata*, for example, are indicative of larger, well-oxygenated water bodies, although other aquatics present are more typical of small ditches, possibly prone to drying. Plant remains point to water-filled ditches with aquatic taxa including duckweed, Water Crowfoot and Water Plantain, with bankside communities of Bulrush, Spike-rush, Celery-leaved Buttercup and Greater Pond-sedge *Carex riparia*. Diatoms provide additional evidence for freshwater conditions notably aerophilous (semi-terrestrial) species such as *Hantzschia amphioxys*, *Pinnularia* spp. and *Navicula mutica*. These are all taxa tolerant of desiccation suggesting that the ditch was subject to drying out.

Terrestrial mollusca show this was a damp, well-vegetated environment next to the ditches, with *Carychium tridentatum*, *Discus rotundatus*, *Aegopinella nitidula* and *Oxychilus cellarius* all indicative of shade, although the absence of any true woodland component to the assemblage indicates a non-wooded environment: tree pollen values are low, and while a shrubby boundary to some ditch sides may have been provided by Bramble and Hazel, the field boundaries do not appear to have been lined with hedges and mature trees as is common today. The ditch sides appear to have supported a rich soil colonised by Nettles with other plants that thrive on rich fertile soils, such as Elder and Fig-leaved

Aerial view of the oval shaped 'summer dike' (Church Field) at Puxton. These small enclosures were built around the 10th century on the surface of a high salt-marsh in order to prevent summer flooding of cultivated areas.

Aerial view of the estuary of the Congresbury Yeo, showing the sea walls constructed to completely protect the North Somerset Levels from tidal inundation. The historic landscape was created behind them through the gradual process of enclosure and drainage as population, and the demand for agricultural land, increased throughout the medieval and post-medieval periods.

53

SR

Blackstones Rhyne, Puxton. Palaeo-environmental assemblages from the excavation of medieval ditches at Puxton, and indeed late Romano-British sites at Banwell Moor and Kenn Moor, reveal very similar fresh-water flora and fauna to that found on the Levels today. The wetland landscapes of the Somerset Levels are highly valued for their ecology, but it is important to remember that these ditches and rhynes are also cultural artefacts and their nature conservation interest is only there because of human engineering and management of the drainage system.

Goosefoot. Other taxa present include damp pasture and meadow species, buttercups *Ranunculus acris/repens/bulbosus*, Hemlock *Conium maculatum* and Hairy Buttercup *Ranunculus sardous*; the pollen assemblage is dominated by grasses, while the mollusca *Vallonia costata* and *Vertigo pygmaea* suggest an environment of long grass/herbs. Annuals of disturbed and waste ground, chickweed, orache, Swine-cress *Coronopus squamatus* and Fat-hen *Chenopodium album* also occur, while pollen includes large numbers of Brassicaceae, plus a range of other weeds of disturbed ground, are suggestive of arable cultivation.

A number of ditches contained dumps of kitchen waste that included cattle, sheep, pig and poultry bones, fish scales and bones, egg shell, plus a well-preserved charred cereal assemblage with wheat dominant but also with barley, rye and oat. Additional field or garden crops include Garden Pea *Pisum sativum* and Celtic Bean *Vicia faba*, which, as rich sources of protein, would have formed an important addition to the diet, as well as being part of the crop rotation system used for improving soil fertility. Large numbers of pollen grains of Brassicaceae, the cabbage family, also occur, but although this family includes domestic brassicas such as cabbage, turnip, rape and mustard, there are weeds like Shepherd's Purse *Capsella bursa-pastoris* that cannot be distinguished from the cultivated crops, and so this pollen could either suggest additional garden crops or weeds from grazed fields or cultivated land. Seeds, capsule and stem fragments from flax were recovered which could have been grown for both its fibre, made into linen, and the seeds which are rich in linseed oil. Documentary sources, notably from the Glastonbury Abbey manors such as Brent also show extensive arable cultivation on the reclaimed Somerset wetlands, though there was also very successful livestock husbandry, including extensive herds of dairy cows and pigs.

This medieval reclamation did not occur throughout the Somerset Levels but was largely restricted to the higher, coastal, alluvial marshes, and while there was some enclosure and drainage of the inland peat bogs, most of these backfens were left unreclaimed. Although they were not cultivated or agriculturally improved, these areas should not be thought of as waste land. The peatlands supported grazing that was sufficiently valued to lead to a series of disputes, for example between the Abbots of Glastonbury and the Dean and Chapter of Wells Cathedral. In 1278 for example the abbot's men destroyed a piggery belonging to the Dean in Godney Moor, and in 1315 the Dean demolished some of the Abbot's walls, dykes and sluices in Blackford and Mark Moors to the west of Wedmore. In 1326 Bishop Drokensford and Abbot Adam of Sodbury agreed to appoint three men to settle the disputed rights within the moors, but just four months later someone set fire to the Abbot's

BOTH PHOTOGRAPHS DB

Now you see it, now you don't. Flooding on Hay Moor in 1994.

peat moors between Burtle Priory and Glastonbury, threatening the abbey itself. The Bishop then excommunicated the Abbot after four of his men allegedly destroyed buildings on his moor of Thealmoor (Tealham Moor), and in the following year the abbot was accused of burning the Dean's timber and grass in Mudgley, and the Dean of destroying houses at Meare and taking trees, 12 horses, 60 oxen, 50 cows, 100 bullocks and 100 pigs worth £200.

In much of the discussion so far, water – in the form of flooding and the need for drainage – has been seen as a problem, and the emphasis has been on removing it from this landscape. It is important, however, to also appreciate that water in many respects was a precious resource. The high water table supported exceptionally fertile pastures. The Somerset Levels supported Glastonbury Abbey's most important herds of cattle and pigs, and a series of artificial canals, such as the Brue, and canalised natural rivers, such as the Axe, were extensively used as a means of communication.

The Somerset Levels and Moors are a supreme example of how the countryside of today is almost wholly hand crafted by generations of human communities: the rich freshwater flora and fauna that are

Above left: The canalised Pilrow Cut as it passes through Mark. While water was a problem when present in too great a quantity, when efficiently managed it was a vital resource providing a means of navigation – as in this 10th/11th century canal – and in keeping the agricultural and grazing land amongst the most fertile in Somerset.

Above right: Woodspring Priory.

so highly valued today are only there because, initially, Romano-British and then medieval communities transformed the intertidal mudflats and salt-marshes. During the medieval period large parts of the Somerset Levels were controlled by the Church, notably Glastonbury Abbey, Wells cathedral, and Woodspring Priory, and these institutions were instrumental in transforming the landscape. Significant areas were in lay hands, notably around Huntspill, Burnham and Kingston Seymour, and the Dissolution of the Monasteries in the 16th century had meant that the great monastic estates, as well as some of those belonging to Wells, were transferred first to the Crown and then to the laity. This enormous upheaval in landownership, however, appears to have had little immediate effect on the Somerset Levels, other than perhaps to make maintenance of the drainage and flood defence systems more difficult because its ownership was fragmented. The late medieval period appears to have seen some enclosure and drainage on the small areas of alluvial soil in the backfens, but the major phase of reclamation was completed by the 14th century by which time all of the coastal, alluvial, marshes were densely settled with only the lowest-lying backfens and raised bog in the Brue Valley left in their natural state. Major changes occurred in these peatlands from the 17th century when there was a national revival in wetland reclamation, but on the alluvial marshes the typical character defining features of today's historic landscape are essentially medieval, and reflect the remarkable achievement of medieval communities.

The Somerset Levels in the Last Two Millennia

Robert Dunning

Thomas Gerard, writing about the market at Langport in the early 17th century, described how people bringing wildfowl for sale in winter across the flooded marshes 'many times missing the Cawsway goe a fishing instead of getting fowle'. Thus still after a thousand years of intensive exploitation and man's best engineering endeavours, nature was still predominant; and flooding will continue in the 21st century to be a feature of the area in spite of current tide-control proposals for the Parrett.

Some two dozen charters dated before the 10th century, mostly granted to Glastonbury abbey, record interest in the area which nearly two centuries later at Domesday was the least densely populated and exploited part of the county. Yet in the next two centuries the monks of Glastonbury in particular, but also the other prominent landowners in the area, the chapter of Wells and the abbeys

Below: Effect on landscape of 40 years of Parliamentary inclosure.
Left: County map 1782. **Right:** County map 1822.

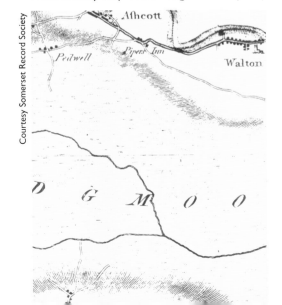

Courtesy Somerset Record Society

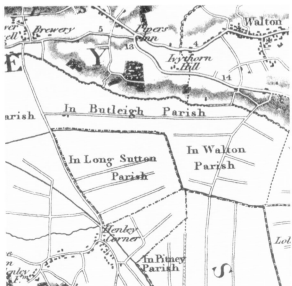

Wells Cathedral.

Glastonbury Abbey.

Wells Cathedral.

of Athelney and Muchelney, and their tenants between them undertook major drainage works and began a process of inclosure which was not completed until the beginning of the 19th century.

Principal among those works must be the diversion of the Brue westwards from Meare Pool to the Parrett, a project undertaken in the later 12th century. Other projects, similarly designed to take water from Meare Pool, involved works to divert water into the Axe from the Sheppey and the Brue, and there were others simply to straighten existing rivers to increase flow either to ease transport or to prevent backing up. Most of those works cannot be precisely dated but are obvious when ancient courses are traced from aerial photographs. Often such diversions entailed the creation of substantial embankments such as Burrow Wall in Othery which accompanied the alteration of the Cary's course in the early 13th century and the causeway between Lyng and Athelney, part of the probably contemporary change to the Tone, which recent archaeological work suggests may have had an earlier phase in the late Saxon period. A much later work involved a cut to avoid a meander in the Parrett at Hamp near Bridgwater, undertaken by Bristol Corporation in 1568. In more modern times first the creation of the King's Sedgemoor Drain and the South Drain under the Brue Drainage Act of 1801 and later still the digging of the Huntspill River in 1940 between them brought a measure of control, reducing but by no means ending flooding.

Large drainage projects were accompanied by the work of small communities and individuals who, initially in return for low rents, created small plots at the moor edge by means of ditching; the rent inevitably rose when the new plots produced good grass. So, on a large scale, Heartymoor and Charlmoor in West Pennard were reclaimed for meadow in the later 13th century. More dramatic still was the cumulative effect of the many small plots around the 'island' of Sowy, where improvement quickly produced high quality grassland which later proved dry enough for arable crops. About 1236 some 272 acres were reckoned as recovered and by 1308 there were well over 200 separate holdings of varying sizes in the three villages of Middlezoy, Othery and Westonzoyland with a total of 250 tenants; and still by 1379 after the devastation of the Black Death there was a taxed population of just over 500 people. Among them were cottagers on the raised banks of the Parrett, established there by 1240.

Other estates followed Glastonbury's example at Sowy and Pennard. By the end of the 14th century there were some 100 acres of new pasture at Cote on Huntspill Mareys manor, but new meadow had been created at Cossington more than a century earlier, at about the time the monks of Muchelney were recovering meadow and pasture grounds on the boundary with Martock. Their estate could now no longer be described simply as the three 'islands' of Domesday Book of which the largest was Muchelney (great island) itself.

Once recovered, of course, landlords could exact economic rents from the 'new' grounds or create dairies or sheep pastures on their home farms. At Butleigh some land called Horsey, inclosed and improved after 1289, produced new rents. At Street inclosure of the moors was still continuing in the

Speed's map of Meare Pool in 1612.

Floods at Muchelney.

59

earlier 14th century but the dairy established as a result was not a success and cows were replaced by sheep. The dairy, on recovered grassland at Northwood on Glastonbury manor in one single year, 1274—5, produced 296 cheeses and 10 stone of butter. Close by the small tenants who had earlier achieved the drainage of Hearty Moor by means of small plots were removed by their landlord, who set up a dairy there in 1347. This was some of the rich grassland which in the later 19th and earlier 20th century made West Pennard a centre for the production of Cheddar and Caerphilly cheese.

There seems to be no doubt that the policies of Glastonbury abbey in particular but also of their neighbours in the Levels had brought the management of the land in central Somerset to a high degree of sophistication and productivity as the result of drainage and management agreements involving shared grazing rights and stocking controls. The removal of most of those controlling landowners at the Dissolution had serious consequences. By the end of the 16th century felling of timber on Glastonbury's moors had reduced their value and the division of ownership brought grazing disputes, tedious and expensive lawsuits, and acrimonious attempts at inclosure which were not finally settled in the parish until 1800. A similar story might be told of places never in Church hands: the huge expanse of Huntspill parish in the 18th century seems to have been divided between a very large number of small tenant farmers interspersed with sizeable areas of common grazing, and in 1777 a survey revealed some 3,000 acres of pasture supporting 2,000 cows and heifers, 1,000 acres mown for hay and then feeding over 4,000 sheep, 1,000 acres grazed by colts and steers. Over 1,000 acres were common grassland. Only 200 acres were arable. For at least thirty years the farmers were said to have been 'caballing' for inclosure, which was achieved in 1782. Typically, the wealthy graziers became wealthier, while the labourers were hardly compensated adequately for loss of common rights.

Elsewhere inclosure of common fields was achieved either by mutual agreement or Act of Parliament in the 17th and 18th centuries in the villages north of the Poldens, sometimes involving improved drainage such as the construction of Moor Rhyne and Land Rhyne in the north of Shapwick parish, effectively creating Shapwick Moor Ground. Schemes in Cossington and Catcott were also entirely successful. To the south of the Poldens the solution was much less simple for the claims to grazing rights on Sedgemoor were more tenaciously held in spite of the promises of the Dutch expert Cornelius Vermuyden. Only when the less successful saw their neighbours' cattle growing fat on improved grounds, and neighbours themselves becoming prosperous in the face of increasing demand for food, could sense prevail. From 1777 a series of Inclosure Acts divided and allotted common moorland, and the Brue Drainage Act of 1801 brought both sides of the Poldens into some sort of

DB

Typical inclosure scenery south of Ivythorn Hill.

TSUNAMI!

The Somerset Levels coastal lowlands typically lie between 5-6m AOD, a height lower than the Spring mean high water in the Severn Estuary. Consequently the Levels are susceptible to flooding from the sea as well as from river sources.

One of the most significant coastal flooding events which affected the Levels and caused the greatest devastation occurred on the morning of the 20th January 1607. This event has previously been regarded by historians as being caused by a large storm, but more recent studies question this and provide evidence that the flood may have been the result of a tsunami. The 1607 event affected an area stretching from the Carmarthenshire coast and Barnstaple northeast along the River Severn as far as Gloucester. It is believed that approximately 2000 people were killed and the region was plunged into economic and social chaos. Much of the documentary evidence relates to Monmouthshire and Somerset and plaques on church walls at Peterstone and Kingston Seymour respectively, and subsequent re-surveying indicates the flood water in these areas may have reached a depth of up to 7-8m.

Several features of the flood reported in contemporary accounts lend support to it being a tsunami event. The event happened at about 9am during apparently fair weather. The sea appears to have been 'driven back' before the wave struck, a classic pre-tsunami feature, and the local inhabitants saw 'afar off as it were in the element huge and mighty hilles of water tombling over one another in such sort as if the greatest mountains in the world had overwhelmed the lowe villages or marshy grounds'. Some imagined 'it had bin some fogge or mist coming with great swiftness towards them and with such a smoke as if mountains were all on fire, and to the view of some it seemed as if myriads of thousands of arrows had been shot forth all at one time'.

Such vivid accounts have led local history writers to regard the flood as being caused by a 'tidal wave'. Bryant & Haslett noted the similarity of the contemporary accounts to more recent descriptions of tsunami events such as those linked to the 1883 Krakatau eruption where the sea was described as 'hilly' and the reference to dazzling, fiery mountains and myriads of arrows is reminiscent of tsunami accounts from Newfoundland in 1929 where the wave crest was like shining car headlights and the 1998 Papua New Guinea wave which was frothing and sparkling.

The speed of the flood event was also significant. One contemporary account refers to a lady that 'before she could get uppe into the higher rooms of her house, having marked the approach of the waters, to have been surprised by them and destroyed, her house being distant above four miles in breadth from the sea'. Another record states that the flood waters were 'affirmed to have runne'. with a swiftness so incredible, as that no gray-hounde could have escaped by running before them'. This suggests a wave crest moving faster than those associated with 'normal' storm surges. Bryant and Haslett have calculated that the 1607 tsunami could have been at least 5.5m high when it struck the Somerset coast and travelled inland as a wave for a distance of some 4km. The maximum inland penetration of the 1607 floodwaters was some 22km as indicated by accounts of the flood reaching the foot of Glastonbury Tor.

Physical evidence of the 1607 tsunami left in the field includes: erosion of large chunks of farmland on the Severn Estuary north of Bristol; the apparently simultaneous widespread deposition of sand layers extending from north Devon to Gloucestershire to the Gower; and large boulders that are only easily moved by tsunami waves, stacked like dominoes at and above the high tide limits all along the coast.

The possible cause of the 1607 tsunami may be an earthquake linked to an active fault system located offshore of southern Ireland. According to Haslett a previously overlooked contemporary account states that an earth tremour was experienced the same morning as the flood event.

Perhaps the most harrowing and evocative visual record of the 1607 tsunami event is captured in a woodcut made about the same time, depicting the flood in the vicinity of what is thought to be Chedzoy Church.

Andy King

economic equality. So the King's Sedgemoor Drain diverted the Cary to discharge into the Parrett at Dunball Clyce and the South Drain was dug to provide a better course for the Brue.

For a short time the South Drain became a commercial waterway linking Glastonbury with the sea at Highbridge, and its successor railway made Highbridge an agricultural, commercial, and engineering centre which would have amazed the first builders of the high bridge. A century later the increasing popularity of road transport killed branch railways, and it is one of the little ironies of history that while most of the Somerset and Dorset line was closed in 1966, that part which linked the main line with Bason Bridge in Huntspill was kept open until 1972 so that materials for the M5 motorway might the more efficiently be delivered.

The improved river courses allowed transport of goods by water and gave people safe passage along river banks. The duties of one particular Glastonbury abbey tenant in the mid 13th century illustrate clearly how, barring floods, the countryside was amazingly accessible. His principal duty was to have an 8-man boat in which he was to carry the abbot, his men, his mobile kitchen, his huntsman and his dogs from Glastonbury as far afield as Godney, Meare and Brent along the Brue in one direction and to Butleigh in the other, to Steanbow along the Whitelake at the far edge of West Pennard, and to Andersey (Nyland) on the Axe. Furthermore he was to carry letters along the Cut and the Axe to Bleadney and Panborough, to manage the wine depot at Steanbow and the vineyard at Panborough, to guard the abbot's fisheries and to maintain the abbot's own boats.

The construction of the Greylake Fosse, perhaps c. 1300, was needed because the prosperous Sowy manor could not then be reached by water from Glastonbury, though by 1280 a watercourse known as Hardingsditch presumably gave access to the Cary and allowed grain to be taken by boat from High Ham to Glastonbury. Glastonbury itself, abbey and town, received both heavy goods and foreign foodstuffs from Bristol, brought by water along the Axe and the Brue to a wharf at Northload.

Further west, where the Parrett and the Tone were the main arteries and Bridgwater the main port of entry, Langport was an inland depot of some importance. A consequence if not the partial purpose of the appearance of Bridgwater bridge c. 1200 was to give the town control of traffic up the Parrett, and the construction of the Langport Slip in 1488 is an indication that river trade was growing. Langport, curiously, was the place where woad, brought overland from Southampton in the 1460s, took to the water for carriage up the Tone and the Parrett to the clothing centres of Taunton and Bridgwater.

Grape harvest.

Rivers, of course, had their own natural hazards and others imposed by man. Heavy goods such as stone from Ham Hill and timber and nails from Bridgwater for use on the construction of Taunton castle in the 1240s could only be brought as far as Ruishton along the Tone, for the shallows there would not permit further progress. More than a century later the hazard was a little lower down river where the abbot of Glastonbury had built a mill at Bathpool on his manor of West Monkton and had planted willows to stabilise the river bank, just as Sir John Poulet had planted on the opposite bank. The width of the river had thus been reduced from 30 feet to 10 feet.

Old pollarded willow.

The building of Ham Mill about 1490 brought the builder, the chapter of Wells, the tenant, the prior of Montacute, and the bishop of Winchester, lord of Ruishton and Taunton, into dispute for Ruishton people complained that it caused their land to be flooded and Taunton merchants weighed in with the argument that passage from Bridgwater was hindered and they could no longer import 'all maner of marchaundyses, corne, cole, stones, and all othre stuff'.

Among others who obviously made a living from river transport was a family of boatmen who occupied a house near the bridge over the Yeo at Long Load by the 1480s where wharves were known forty years earlier. That family, the Bradfords, grew to become the dominant carriers of heavy goods by water and land; another business depending heavily on trade by water and based at Langport came, as Stuckey and Bagehot, to be at the end of the 18th century traders with London, Birmingham, Liverpool and Manchester and by the 1860s to be owners of 14 East Indiamen and 19 barges, and of a bank which had a note circulation second only to that of the Bank of England.

St Michael's, Burrow Mump.

The value of the Levels in historic times is easy to demonstrate, notably in the Middle Ages from the various manorial accounts of the Glastonbury abbey estate; the abbey was the second richest religious house in the country in 1535, and more than half of that income came from its estates in central Somerset. In the later Middle Ages the abbey's large sheepflocks went from one estate to another: there were just over 400 wethers and hoggs c.1354 at Butleigh, a year earlier a flock of half the size, mainly ewes, was moved from Glastonbury to Street. Those ewes were presumably part of the flock of 1,231 sheep brought together a few weeks earlier at Glastonbury for shearing.

Cheese and butter, wool and honey, grain, fowl and fish were the obvious and significant products of the land. Tenants at Butleigh, for instance, produced six sesters of honey between them in 1171 and so did tenants at Ashcott and Sowy; a century later there were eight hives of bees at Sowy. As for fowl,

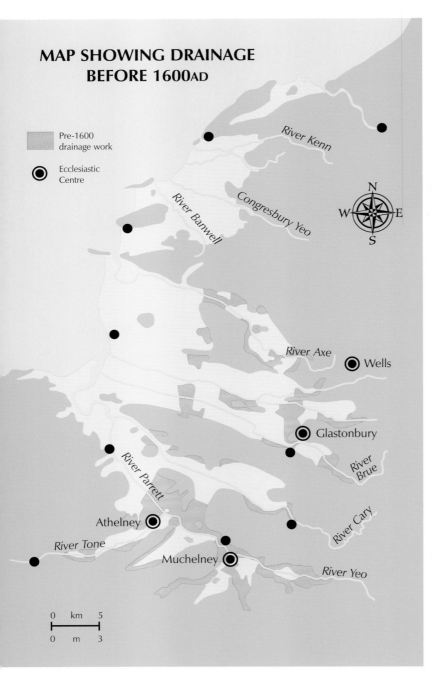

MAP SHOWING DRAINAGE BEFORE 1600AD

Pre-1600
drainage work

Ecclesiastic
Centre

River Kenn

River Banwell

Congresbury Yeo

N
W E
S

River Axe

Wells

Glastonbury

River Brue

River Parrett

River Cary

Athelney

River Tone

Muchelney

River Yeo

0 km 5

0 m 3

Pair of Mute Swans.

rents were paid in cranes for a farm at Greylake in the late 12th century; a flock of peafowl was kept at Sowy in the later 13th; and there were swanneries at Edington and Meare. At the second there were 90 swans c.1540, most of them described as old. Herons and pheasants were noted in the woods at Meare at the same time. Fowling in the Middle Ages involved the use of nets; from the later 17th century onwards sophisticated decoy pools appeared, one on Aller Moor in 1676, another belonging to High Ham in 1682, a third at Meare by 1685, a fourth at Dundon in 1695. The builder of the last, Thomas Strangways, took Mallard, Teal and Widgeon there, but found that netting for the tunnels, staff costs, powder and shot, hempseed to attract the birds' attention and food for the dog to lead them up the pipes took much of the profit. Snipe were paid at Glastonbury as rent for hunting rights on Hulkmoor.

Fisheries had been recognised as a valuable asset at Domesday: two paid 6,000 eels at Muchelney and there were other fisheries at Meare, Creech St Michael, North Curry and Wedmore in or on the edges of the Levels. A century later, one at Marchey owed 7,000 eels to the Glastonbury abbey cellarer. In one year in the late 13th century the Meare fishery, obviously including Meare Pool, produced 224 sticks of eels, 30 great eels, 55 pike, 200 bream, and about 120 'white' fish, but as the pool decreased in size, so did the yield. Part may have remained permanently under water until the first decade of the 18th century.

RB

Another important natural resource, long pre-dating garden peat, was turf for fuel. In the later 13th century the lord of Edington manor made a grant to one man of eight waggon-loads of turf for a year with the right to sell and gave another as much as five men could dig in two days. A third grantee seems to have had licence to dig whenever he chose. Six centuries on and parishioners of Cossington, Stawell and Woolavington had somehow established rights there. Others were doing business in Catcott and the owner of the Edington estate saw clearly that money was to be made, by 1651 charging a fee on turf carts going from there to Mark and Huntspill. Later in the same century at Shapwick both turves and tufts of matted grass called hassocks were being dug, the latter considered as good as turves for brewing. Large quantities of turves were taken in the 19th century: Edington in the 1870s had five turf merchants and eleven cutters, Catcott 13 dealers, Ashcott eleven. At Shapwick 'great quantities' of peat were being dug and by 1889 the Eclipse Peat Manufacturing Co. based at Ashcott was producing moss horse litter and firelighters from the turbary alongside the traditional extractors. The work of generations of turfcutters, no longer politically correct, has been within its limited area of operation of greater significance than traditional agriculture.

The Fish House at Meare.

DB

One important casualty of the inclosure of the moors over time has been woodland. Hearty Moor on the north side of West Pennard parish was described about 1135 as 'a splendid and ample alder grove' and in the 1320s was so thick that animals could not be pastured there. Timber was regularly cut for fuel, fencing and building and the alders were all gone by 1500. Perhaps more dramatic was the fate of woodland in Baltonsborough. In 1310 North and South woods, mostly oak and thorn, measured together 220 acres, and there were smaller alder woods providing fuel to heat Glastonbury Abbey. In the early 16th century the two woods measured 800 acres, but the oak there had not been well tended and produced only 2,600 faggots a year. Both by the later 17th century had been ruined through overstocking and both were inclosed. By the end of the 18th century there was no wood in the parish. In Glastonbury parish alders on Kennard and North moors grew too thick for cattle but provided good fuel and by the mid 16th century alder and willow on South or Alder moor was also used for hop poles. A lease of 1584 required the tenant to plant 600 willows within six years. Hulkmoor produced oak timber up to 1640, largely used for charcoal. Inclosure of the moors before the end of the century spelled the end of the woodland there.

Glastonbury looking across flooded site of Meare Pool.

Grass, hay, grain, reeds, cheese, fatstock including goats, poultry, game: the Levels have provided an amazingly rich harvest in spite of floods and occasional inaccessibility to the present day. Early in the 19th century one other sight was common and was graphically remembered by William Quekett of Langport:

> In the summer months the moor appears covered as with snow. This appearance is caused by the immense flocks of geese which are fed there chiefly for the sake of the feathers and quills. One goosier will own as many as 3,000 geese. Every year the poor creatures are plucked as closely as a cook would pluck them before roasting; and the quills and feathers form a profitable source of income to their masters. Every night the flocks of geese are driven into enclosures and fed, being allowed to wander again on the moor in the early morning.

(W. Quekett, My Sayings and Doings (1888), 27—8).

This article is based on research published in *Victoria History of Somerset, volumes iii, iv, vi*, and *viii* and on the unpublished MS to be published in 2006 as volume IX.

'SALT OF THE EARTH'

Rock salt was discovered beneath Puriton accidentally in 1910 during a private exploration for coal! A borehole drilled 631 metres into the red Triassic mudstones found no coal but from 183 metres there were over 36 metres of strata rich in salt.

Commercial extraction began in 1911. The salt was dissolved by water fed down boreholes 0.375 metres in diameter and the resulting brine was pumped into a roofed storage reservoir at the surface. From there it was gravity-fed into three shallow boiling pans. Evaporation yielded crystals from which fine table salt and a coarser industrial product were obtained.

The plant operated on a 24 hour, 5 day a week, basis with the pans being cleaned at weekends. There was employment on a 3-shift system for 20 – 30 people, their wages comparing favourably with local agricultural rates.

In 1922 the Dunball Salt Works (or 'the Treacle Mines' as they were known locally!) became a victim of economic recession. The national 'Salt Union' to which it then belonged closed it, presumably to safeguard employment and production in Cheshire. Demolition and clearance of the Works followed.

The Dunball site is near the southern margin of the Somerset salt field which in turn underlies the central Somerset wetlands. It is estimated that the area may lie above a reserve of 13 000 million tonnes of rock salt.

Derek Briggs

A 1982 photograph of the concrete brine-storage reservoir above the site of the Dunball Salt Works (1911 – 1922). It was 52.5 metres long, 4.5 metres across and 1.5 metres deep. The site is now private land and totally overgrown.

Irrigation of the Somerset Levels

Francis Farr-Cox

When the subject of the Somerset Levels and Moors comes up, the talk is often of flood defence schemes and drainage channels. There are, however, many other aspects such as irrigation, wet fencing (stock proof ditches) and the summer pen (holding high summer water levels with sluices) which perhaps contribute even more to the peculiar nature of this landscape. It is these aspects and their origins that I want to discuss in more detail.

To understand the 'system', it is important to have a basic knowledge of the causes of flooding and other aspects. Flooding on the Moors is generally derived from the surrounding uplands with the added complications of a flat lowland landscape and tide-locked rivers. Tide-lock occurs when the high tides of the Bristol Channel prevent the rivers discharging to the sea and river water, including flood water, has to be stored in the freshwater system for up to eight hours in the day. The Moors themselves are actually a low rainfall area by south-west standards with a rain total that is more typical of the London area. A consequence of successful drainage means that, without sluices, all the water would drain away and there would be no wet fencing or cattle watering in summer. This then is the reason for the summer pen. If evapo-transpiration is high, a source of fresh water fed into the moor is also needed, and so, inlets and feed channels bring water from the embanked rivers to top up the rhynes and ditches. Having grown up in this environment it does not seem peculiar to me. I well recall, though, a discussion I had with a colleague, a river engineer who had worked for many years in East Anglia, who moved to take up a similar post in Somerset. The two jobs, ostensibly the same, had proved to be very different. In East Anglia his workload had been most intense during periods of heavy rain. Whilst Somerset could offer similar events, it was the routine management of summer water levels that presented the greatest challenge each year, literally come rain or shine!

RW

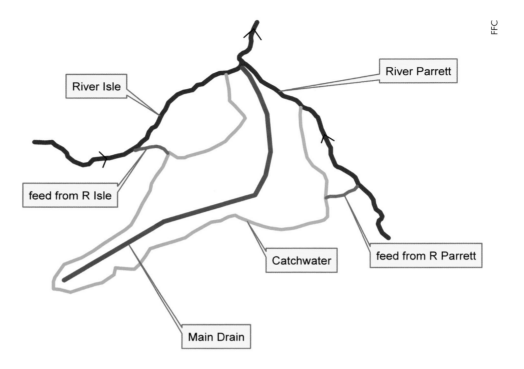

FFC

FFC

Small water level management structure.

I wanted to discover what was known about the history of the non-drainage infrastructure such as the water feeds, inlets and summer sluices. I turned initially, despite its title, to Michael Williams' book *The Draining of the Somerset Levels*. Published in 1970, it seems very strange that this classic work went out of print just as real national interest in the Levels and Moors began. Williams deals with much more than pure drainage and refers to many contemporary sources. I wanted to glean my information from these and from some of the original Acts of Enclosure and Drainage. The period of most relevance for the peat Moors was the 100 years between 1750 and 1850. It was in this period that the Moors were transformed into the landscape that we have inherited today.

In 1750 the coastal Levels and the peat Moors would have appeared distinctly different though today they look, at least superficially, so similar. At that time, the landscape of the coastal clay areas was laid out with its network of rhynes much as today, though the area was probably more open with far fewer hedges. Inland the peat Moors were very different; un-drained tracts of common land with few if any rhynes or ditches.

My search for relevant contemporary accounts started with the *Letters and Papers of the Bath & West of England Society* which was founded in 1777. The authors of letters were not confined to the West of England and the various articles give a real flavour of the agricultural revolution. One of the most influential local letter contributors was Richard Locke of Burnham. His writings confirm that drainage was just one of several drivers for agricultural improvement in Somerset. They also shed an interesting light on how the peat moors came to be improved primarily through the efforts of local people in an area where the famous 'drainer' Sir Cornelius Vermuyden had been rejected.

Locke had greatly increased his social standing and personal wealth by fastidiously improving the small farm that he had inherited. He describes his work on his land in an enthusiastic style that's full of missionary zeal to encourage others to follow in his footsteps. Born and living in Burnham myself I can't help feeling that Locke would be disappointed to see the current state of some of the local fields. One particular problem he identified, still evident today, was poor surface drainage. The main cause was a raised lip around each field where the arisings were repeatedly dumped when the ditches were cleaned out. This poor drainage, coupled with years of mowing for hay resulted in a very impoverished soil. Locke's solution involved re-profiling the field, planting legumes for several seasons and finally re-guttering and re-sowing grass. With success Locke bought more land which he improved and soon he was looking to apply his experience to improve the peat Moors inland for agriculture. Farming as advocated by Locke and others was a threat to the commoners who grazed the Moors. It is interesting to note that Locke was burned in effigy for promoting his ideas, a form of protest which was to be reversed in the 1980s when farmers in turn thought their liveli-hoods were threatened when SSSIs were declared on the Moors.

Improving soil and promoting good husbandry were also reasons for enclosure. The nature of the commons meant that there was unlimited grazing, at least in stock numbers, and it is recorded that in 1775 there were 30 000 cattle on King's Sedgemoor.

Rhyne on West Moor.

The Revd William Quekett, writing about West Sedgemoor in the early 1800s, recalled that
in the summer months the moor appears covered as with snow. This appearance is caused by the immense flocks of geese which are fed there chiefly for the sake of their feathers and quills. One goosier will own as many as 8 000 geese.

How appropriate that West Sedgemoor is now home to a major RSPB reserve!

The actual Acts of Parliament which enabled commissioners to improve the moors often reveal the areas of concern in their preamble. Cutting new channels certainly helped to drain the land but many of the side channels were cut primarily as boundary markers dividing commons between parishes. The idea was to divide up the commons and so improve land management. Ditches were a practical boundary marker and cheaper than other methods. The Act which enabled the draining and enclosure of King's Sedgemoor in 1791 allowed the commissioners "to make or cause to be made ditches of sufficient depth and width to incompass, drain, fence and inclose each and every of the said parishes or hamlets". Nowadays many people do not realise that many rhynes were dug primarily as boundary markers and for this reason some are not in the best place for effective drainage or irrigation. Even in the 20th century the various portions of Kings Sedgemoor were detached portions of the various parishes. Today, everything has been simplified but the old boundary rhynes still bear their parish names, and blocks of land are still known by names like the Shapwick Allotments, showing that they were the portion allotted to that parish and which, for a time, formed part of it. There is very little in the King's Sedgemoor Act about irrigation by name but there is a clause giving "power to make or erect engines or sluices". The Act also involved the diversion of the River Cary into the Moor perhaps to provide one of the first irrigation systems on the peat moors.

The Brue Act of 1801 did have more clear provision to provide for summer water. In this case there was a pressure group for it. Before the passing of the Act the Brue provided quite effective drainage for the coastal clay levels but not from the peat moors which were in places somewhat lower than the coastal clay. Plans to improve peat land drainage were viewed with suspicion by some coastal farmers. John Billingsley in *A General view of the Agriculture of the County of Somerset*, published at that time, wrote that "many of the proprietors in Huntspill Marsh will object if their land be made too dry in the summer and their stock destitute of water". He noted that their objections could be overcome by providing hatches. Indeed part of the Brue Act included that "doors be erected to keep up freshwater in dry seasons".

In 1833 one of the last moor enclosure Bills was passed for West Moor, East Moor and Middle Moor near Midelney. By this time it would appear that the need for irrigation had been clearly recognised and special provision for this was included. The Act was for the "better and more effectual draining and improving the said moors and commons hereby intended to be divided or allotted or any part or parts thereof, or for the better and more effectual irrigating and watering or supplying with water any of the allotments...". For the latter purpose it would be "lawful to award order and direct any

West Moor Pumping Station.

R Parrett inlet to West Moor from the Bur Reed on the right of the picture.

Opposite page: Lapwing. RW

streams of water, watersprings or watercourses to go or be turned in or diverted through over or across any part of the said moors ... for the watering or supplying with water or drainage of the several allotments...".

A close examination of the detail of the West Moor proposals shows a central channel to the River Isle for drainage. For irrigation the whole moor is surrounded by a catchwater fed with water from the River Isle to the west and the River Parrett to the east. This is the situation that continues more or less to the present day. It is in my opinion the best planned Somerset moor.

Today all the other Moors and much of the Levels work in similar vein, with a system of summer feeds, from the often embanked rivers. Within the rhyne network some channels are primarily for drainage and some for irrigation. The majority of channels perform both functions as needs demand. The feeds from the rivers are often submerged and positioned in out of the way places. This is the part of the network that is the least well known. Some feeds are very obscure and I wonder if a proportion were 'retro-fitted' to earlier drainage schemes as the need for summer water became apparent.

Today, water level management is more important than ever with the complex problem of delivering the 'right' water level for the favourable status of Site of Special Scientific Interest (SSSI), the need to supply different farming requirements and to protect buried archaeology. There is also a need generally to conserve soils for the future and prevent peat shrinkage which can complicate both drainage and irrigation. On this latter point it is interesting to note that a survey for the Brue Act of 1801 shows peat lands in part of the Brue valley were actually above the spring high tide level 200 years ago!

In spite of its importance, maintenance of the summer pen and the associated irrigation system still seems to be the poor relation of drainage. Since their original construction, most drainage channels have been widened and many fitted with pumps. In contrast, many inlets still have gear dating from the 19th century. These old structures are remarkable survivors with heritage value. They provide an important link to the past history of the Moors but, is the historic irrigation system capable of delivering the water efficiently for today's needs? Global warming is often cited as a reason to look at more effective flood defence provision. More prolonged droughts could pose an even greater threat if water resources and the irrigation system are inadequate to sustain this historic landscape. Agricultural livelihoods, hidden archaeology and unique biodiversity would all be at risk.

Detail of the structure on the R Isle inlet to West Moor giving the construction date of 1861.

Living with Peat

Roger Rogers

My name is Roger Rogers – I always say we were so poor my Mother couldn't afford two names. In fact it was a bit of a trend at the time, at one school (and I went to 5 different ones, whilst living in the same house, the boundaries kept changing) there was a Robert Roberts and a William Williams.

I am going to try to give a flavour of life on the levels 50 yrs ago. I was born on August 19th 1949 at the station house, beside the Glastonbury canal (now the south drain) and the railway track. Now all these features have disappeared. On this day, 56 yrs ago, the train derailed and slid into the canal. It was the Somerset and Dorset, (nicknamed Slow and Dirty or Serene and Delightful).

My father and eldest brother worked on the peat, with Mother's help. My brothers were 15 and 16 yrs older than me, I was the accidental menopause baby, so was taken to work with them from an early age. My first memory was of falling into a rhyne (pronounced reen) with my wheelbarrow made by my brother Dennis (a carpenter).

I was more concerned for my wheelbarrow than myself, it was my most treasured possession at the age of 3yrs. I think I was a happy child but may have proved a bit of a handful for my elderly parents, who regularly shut me out of the house on Sundays for disrupting Sunday lunch. We always had a joint of meat on Sunday and it would be made to last for most of the week. We had no running water in our house. The train brought us a five gallon churn once a day, so we learned to be economical with water.

My father was born the 10th child in a two roomed cottage in 'Hithy'(Heathway Drove), and he followed his father as a peat digger.

GR

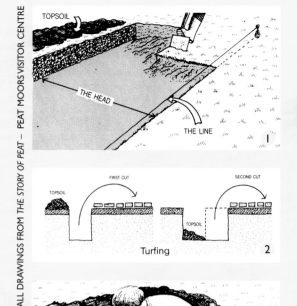

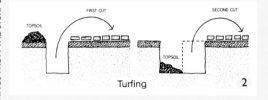

Turfing

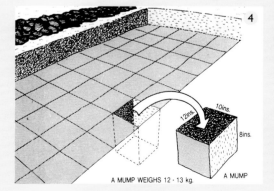

A MUMP WEIGHS 12 - 13 kg.

1: Lining out the head & unridding.
2: Turfing.
3: Benching & stooling with a turf scythe.
4: Benching & stooling into mumps
5: Winrowing

Right: Hand cut peat.

Below: Peat ruckles.

74

Peat digging developed its own terminology;

- We 'lined-out' the ground we were about to cut with a garden line (string and markers). The line had to be straight.

- 'Unridding' was the name we gave to the process of clearing the topsoil from the peat to be dug.

- Marking out the 'head' was the next stage. How many blocks or 'mumps width would determine the size, e.g. a 5 mump head or 7 mump head. This is done with a turf -scythe, the process known as 'benching and stooling' (the vertical lines like benches, the horizontal ones crossing looking like stools.)

- Mumps are then separated and dug out with a turf-digging spade, much like a garden spade but the handle at a more acute angle. The blocks are then placed beside the pit. Each sodden mump measures 10 by 8 by 12 inches and weighs approx 28 lbs. This process takes a great amount of strength especially in the back. It is literally back-breaking work.

- Each mump is then put into rows or 'lanes' (known as 'bearing-back', this was my mother's job, she used a 'four-pronged pick', a bit like a hay-fork) then each mump is slit into three 'turves' with a chopper (another special round-headed tool made for the purpose).

- The turves are then left for 10 days to dry out. Then they are 'pulled-up' or turned on to their ends to dry. This would often be a job for children before or after school.

- The next stage was 'winrowing', where semi-dry turves were stacked in threes so air could blow between them. These would make long lines across the fields.

- Two to three weeks later the blocks will be built into 'ruckles' the familiar bee-hive structures, made of about 1 000 blocks, the dry ones inside, damper ones on the outside to dry. The blocks or turves could over-winter here. Once a turf is dry it can never absorb water again. A 'tate' is a small version of a ruckle.

- The blocks remaining too damp would be made into 'hyles' a 14 block structure, made to a very specific design to maximise drying area of each block.

Saw-sedge
Cladium mariscus

Saw-Sedge or Great Fen-sedge *Cladium mariscus* is a major component of Somerset fen peat and it is still grown in East Anglia as a strong thatching material, especially for roof ridges. It is now rare in Somerset: two out of three sites are probably introductions.

Graham Rix

Old picture of Roger's family, c.1914. **From Left:** Aaron Difford, Harry Rogers (Uncle), Edwin Rogers (Grandfather), Edmund George Rogers (father of Roger Rogers).

Some common words often used in the wetlands of Somerset

Dunwithies = White Willow or Goat Willow
Oller = Alder
Dunflies = horseflies
Emmetts = ants
Gramferjigs = woodlice
Lady-dish-dash = Pied-wagtail
Withy-wind = Bind-weed
Snake-pipe = Mare's-tails (*Equisetum*)
Scrammed = cold (freezing)

Dumpsy-dark = twilight
Ray-balling = catching eels
Wally (drove) = wallway
Hithy = heathway
Westy = Westhay dunkey = donkey hoss = horse
S'now = you know
Dree-pen-north = 3 pennyworth
Drove = a lane or trackway

Roger Rogers

When we had school parties or groups I would teach them 'hyling', they had lots of fun learning this, often the less academic children found they were really good at it. We even had a Womens' Institute group who really enjoyed themselves. Twenty five blocks in a basket would cost 2s 6d, (it stayed this price for quite a few years during the 1950s and 1960s).

Peat work would only last through the summer months so my dad would have to get other work in the winter. He would work for farmers cleaning out ditches. He called this 'scouring', which he did with a long straight scythe called a 'boucher'. Another job would be mole-catching. Moles were known as 'wants', so he would go 'wanting'. He would skin the moles and hang their skins out to dry. Then he would send them away to a mole-skin manufacturer. Dad was also a good shot, as are my brother Ken and youngest son Michael who has shot for England. Any duck or pheasant which flew across the railway track he claimed was his and we either had it to eat or he would barter it for a joint of meat at a butcher's in Bridgwater.

During the war my Dad didn't really have enough to eat, he ended up with a paralysed shoulder which he was convinced was to do with malnutrition. He was exempt from call-up because he was one of the fastest diggers. Peat was needed for putting on runways, Dad said, during the war. There was some bad feeling about this in the village. Some peat workers switched to farm work thinking they would avoid call-up and they didn't, so Dad staying home annoyed a few people. He would always

PHC

Pheasant.

77

Willow 'stools' in winter.

The growing crop.

Harvesting.

BASKET WILLOW – OSIERS
Salix viminalis

The first willow (withy) bed was planted on West Sedgemoor in 1810. In Victorian times it was used for wicker furniture, baskets, bath chairs and beehives but 1919 it was mainly used for baskets. The process of willow growing is labour intensive; it needs a high water table but in hot summers with moderate rainfall it can grow up to 2.5 cm a day. The product is strong, environmentally friendly and aesthetically very attractive.

Pat Hill-Cottingham

Willow bundles ready to be colllected and processed.

The stripping machine.

Withies after stripping and dying.

Canes drying on racks.

Basket maker.

Left: Canes ready for use.

keep a kitchen garden and we always had a pig. He had acquired his own small plot of peat at the age of 16 and he started working for himself in 1945.

My parents bought 'The Willows' at Westhay in 1963 (also the year I left school). It was a small cottage and a peat-ground. We dug out the peat, then later the pit was backfilled with topsoil from a nearby site. By 1976, demand had increased for peat 'and we began the garden centre; we had already begun to sell peat by the roadside for a few years. Also at this time, in 1982, the visitors centre became the Somerset Levels Museum, the brainchild of Dr John Coles. Our children would rush back from school and cycle down to the Sweet track 'dig', a few fields just behind our house where they would watch enthralled as bits of the ancient roadway were revealed.

We left the moors in 1990, but I still returned to do a bit of demonstration peat-digging at the Visitor's Centre, trying to pass on some skills to my sons and whoever wanted to watch.

His childhood home.

RW

Kestrel.

Sharpham Moor Plot – Somerset's most historic reserve

Graham Rix

This 1.3 acre field about two miles west of Glastonbury usually fails to excite visitors on first acquaintance. There is much more to it than meets the eye: it is believed to be southern England's oldest nature reserve after Wicken Fen. Records of its plant life started in 1915 and continue to the present and it has been managed for ecology rather than agriculture from the 1950s onwards. It was originally typical of the area but now strongly contrasts with it as it is surrounded by peat workings destined to become a leisure lake in which it is to be the tip of an odd-shaped peninsula.

The Clifton botanist H Stuart Thompson found a hybrid sedge previously unrecorded in Britain growing there in 1915. It is called *Carex X evoluta* and is the hybrid between Greater Pond Sedge *C.riparia* and Slender Sedge *C. lasiocarpa*. It was unrecorded after his death in1940, rediscovered in 1955 but not found there between 1970 and the present. However, the good news is that it was found by Myra Collins at nearby Street Heath in the mid 1990s and, after formal permission from English Nature, Somerset Wildlife Trust plans to reintroduce it on its original site. The great Cambridge botanist Prof. A G Tansley (who coined the word 'ecosystem') saw the plot as an opportunity for studies of plant succession and he provided £20 of the £45 to buy the plot in 1923. It was owned by the Society for the Promotion of Nature Reserves, which became RSNC and is now The Wildlife Trusts. They passed it to SWT in 1999.

Roe Deer. GR

Professor Sir AG Tansley, the distinguished Cambridge botanist at Sharpham Moor plot on 23rd June 1923, photographed by H Stuart Thompson. They noted about a hundred species of flowering plants, characteristic of the levels, including the rare hybrid sedge whose site, Thompson in particular, wished to preserve. Tansley stressed the potential for long-term studies of plant succession.

In June 1923 Thompson and Tansley visited the site and recorded 98 species of flowering plants in a couple of hours, took a photograph and drew a sketch-map on a laundry ticket. There was a long clearing in the SW corner and a central peat cutting with Reedmace. Beyond this was willow/alder scrub. In the war years the whole plot was carr woodland. Dr. J. F. Hope-Simpson of Bristol University was warden in the 1950s and 60s and he supervised the clearance and maintenance of a U-shaped glade and a peat slope. This plan was continued when, in 1970, Somerset County Council leased the site for field studies. The area had plenty of woodland and pasture. The associated pumping of water for peat extraction, which was becoming mechanised and increasing, tended to leave the plot high and dry. This drying was prevented from the worst extremes by the peat extractor being required by the planners to maintain water in our ditches as a condition of permission to extract. To enable grazing, the whole of the front of the plot has been cleared and fenced while the NW part remains undisturbed woodland.

The isolation has produced single examples of various species which may have been in the seedbank or arrived by other means. These 'one-offs' include English Elm, Sycamore, Bluebell, Twayblade and Yew. The wood has the Scarlet Cup fungus *Sarcoscypha coccinea,* Fly Agaric occurs under the big birch and we have had the Earthstar *Geastrum triplex* for several years. Some of the typical plants are Reed, Yellow Iris, Angelica, Tormentil, Skullcap, Hemp Agrimony, Hemp Nettle, Marsh Woundwort, Ragged Robin, Comfrey, Meadowsweet. Insects, especially dragonflies, are well represented and Barn Owl, Kingfisher, Little Egret, Badger and Roe Deer have visited the reserve.

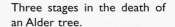

Three stages in the death of an Alder tree.

Far left: The tree with one main branch from low down on the trunk. Taken in March 1973, it has fallen about 45° to the left, its branches mingling with those of its neighbours.

Left: The end of January 1974 shows it down to 25° or 30°, having also rotated towards the viewer.

Below left: April 1980 shows the trunk horizontal, but still clear of the ground over a shallow old peat cutting. By the summer of 1989, it was rotting and half buried. In 1996 it could be seen as a ridge on the ground. In 2000 there was no visible trace.

83

SERC

EN

SERC

1948   1971   1994

Sharpham Moor Plot and its environs from the air: 1948, 1971 and 1994

The same time interval – 23 years – separates each view from the next. There is a striking similarity between the first two, representing very little change.

Loading Batch Farm is due south of the Plot and a natural stream runs by, two fields to the south-east. Most fields are either woodland or hay/pasture. The straight trenches formed by mechanical peat extraction are only on two sites in the south-west in 1971. By 1994, they have replaced all but a few fields in the south-east and virtually all woodland except for the nature reserves. The north-west block is Street heath. The farm and stream have gone and there is a large peat works in the south-west corner. Since then, nearly half of Street Heath and two thirds of Sharpham Moor Plot have been felled to limit water loss and encourage wetland plants. The Plot has benefited from a clay bank next to its north-east boundary. A new access from the drove to the north has been started and the drove beyond the Plot has been removed. The surrounding workings will be a leisure lake with the Plot in the middle.

Peat Moors Centre – The story so far

Eddie Wills

The story of the archaeology and natural history of the Somerset Levels and Moors has fascinated residents and visitors to the area for over a hundred years. The discovery of Glastonbury Lake Village in 1892 marked the start of over a century of archaeological research in the wetlands of Somerset. Detailed excavations, analysis of human activity, waterlogged wooden objects and organic remains have enabled us to produce a picture of what life was like in Somerset over the past 6000 years. Analysis of buried pollen, insects and other environmental evidence has built up a picture of the parallel changes in the landscape.

Today we continue to use and modify the area for our own needs. The continuation of the Peat Industry and the restoration of worked out peat lands for nature conservation interests perpetuates the cycle of reed bed formation and the need for water level management.

Understanding these issues requires detailed interpretation. Part of the role of the Peat Moors Centre at Westhay is to explain how the Somerset Levels and Moors have developed and how they continue to adapt to modern requirements. The Centre is ideally situated to enable access to Shapwick Heath National Nature Reserve to see how archaeology, nature conservation, the peat industry and water level management are all interconnected.

The site was established as a small archaeological display in 1982 by the Somerset Levels Project, directed by John and Bryony Coles. They had approached the then owner of the Willows Garden Centre, Roger Rogers about hosting a local display of their findings, as most items were being sent further afield for conservation. This fitted well with Roger Rogers own plans, as he wished to display his family's collection of peat-turf cutting tools. And so the Peat Moors Visitor Centre came into being.

GR

Cooking in the roundhouse.

With financial assistance from Somerset County Council (SCC), the Centre was greatly expanded in 1992 to celebrate the centenary of the discovery of the Glastonbury Lake Village. This expansion involved relocating the display elements on the site and the construction of two roundhouses, based on evidence from the Lake Village, with representations of some of the ancient trackways recreated in a peat cut. Bulleid and Gray's original site hut from the Meare Lake Village excavations was set up by the County Museum Service with panels to tell the story of the discovery of the settlement. These are supplemented by a selection of artefacts associated with that excavation. The site went on to win the British Archaeological Awards for the Presentation of Archaeological Information to the Public for that year.

The Visitor Centre came under the full control of SCC's Environment Department in October 1994, prior to the purchase of the entire site in 1996. Since that time the Centre has continued to develop in an entirely organic way. Available space prevents major expansion of the Centre, but the nature

Roundhouse under construction.

Above: Completed roundhouse and dug-out canoe.

Top right: Tools exhibited.

Right: Dying wool.

of the materials of its constructs means that it is always in a state of change. Over the years projects have included a dug-out canoe based on an example found only yards away on Shapwick Heath in 1906; pottery kilns and furnaces for smelting iron and bronze; a four-post grain store cum chicken shed and a number of temporary shelters.

During the 2003 season the Centre began a course of remodelling, brought on by the need to replace the sheds that had contained the principle displays since 1982. The primary role of the Centre has always been to interpret the local monuments, especially those, which because of their fragile nature, cannot be seen in situ. With this in mind the focus was brought back firmly to local discoveries with an increased emphasis on the reconstructed elements rather than static displays, in order to provide a hub for exploration of the area's unique archaeological heritage. This ongoing programme dovetails with the Avalon Marshes Heritage Network of panels and interpretation of the wider landscape to provide a complete experience for visitors and students.

As part of the remodelling, a new roundhouse was constructed in 2004. This building of approximately 8 metres in diameter, was based on Mound IX from Glastonbury Lake Village. The building was selected on two counts; it's shape, strictly more oval than round, thereby providing an interesting contrast with the existing houses, and it's unusual hearth or table, a rectangular mound of clay roughly a metre and a half square and decorated with 67 'cup rings'. Experience gained from the construction and observation of the 'behaviour' of the existing roundhouses proved invaluable. One innovation has been the creation of a smoke vent above the front door to allow smoke to escape above head height. Experiments with this are still ongoing, but the vent has not drawn the fire to the extent that the roof is set alight! Construction of the building was featured, albeit briefly, in the recent SSC 'What the Ancients did for us' series.

Each year well over 2000 school children visit the site as part of organised school trips to learn something of wattle and daub and wetland archaeology in the Centre's mock dig, but these only account for about a quarter of the Centre's annual visitors. The Centre also continues to run a range of ancient technology courses with topics ranging from fletching to bronze casting and a two day coracle building course which is always over subscribed. The up-swell of interest in home grown archaeology in recent years ensures the continuing popularity of the Centre and we can only hope that this will see the Peat Moors Centre project continue to develop for another twenty years.

EW

Weaving.

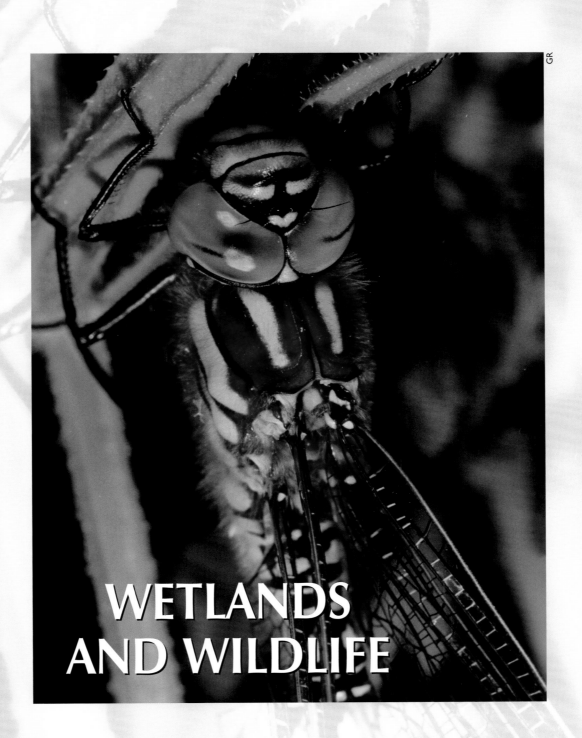

GR

WETLANDS AND WILDLIFE

Water and Wildlife

Martin Drake

Britain's high rainfall and extensive low-lying areas provide the basis for rich wetlands. Although now sadly drained, there remains about 5000 km^2 of land in the UK Ramsar sites of international importance for their wetland flora and fauna (including extensive estuarine land). Somerset is particularly well endowed with lowland wetlands compared with much of Britain. Lowland wet grassland alone occupies about 35,000 ha of the county, and the Somerset Levels and Moors are the largest expanses of lowland wet grassland in the UK.

Wetlands cover a wide range of habitats where water is clearly the key feature above all else. Fens, bogs, river, ponds and carr woodland are more than just aquatic habitats. The dichotomy between aquatic and 'terrestrial' systems is actually an artificial convenience created by biologists, and does not match reality. When this division is disregarded, we find that a large fraction of our flora and fauna is dependent upon wetland habitats. There is obviously a gradient in the wetness required by plants and animals, so no precise figure can be given to the numbers of species reliant on wetlands.

As an example, take two large groups of Britain's beetles that are not thought of as aquatic species, the 350 species of ground beetles and 1000 species of rove beetles. About half the ground beetles and about 40% of the rove beetles are entirely or mostly reliant on wetlands. Analysis of a similar number of flies produces the same result: about half are wetland species. If this large sample is indicative of the whole fauna, it is clear that the proportion of the fauna (and possibly flora) associated with wetlands is disproportionately large in comparison with the area of such habitats left in the country. This highlights the importance of water to our wildlife.

Opposite page: Black tailed Godwit.

GR

THE IMPORTANCE OF NATURE CONSERVATION

The Somerset Levels and Moors are the largest area of lowland wet grassland, coastal and floodplain grazing marsh and associated wetland habitats remaining in Britain today. They cover approximately 60 000 hectares in the floodplains of the rivers Axe, Brue, Parrett and Tone and supports a wide variety of wetland plants and animals.

The Moors are of outstanding nature conservation importance for their rich and varied mosaic of wet grasslands, reed-beds, mires and fen meadows separated by a complex network of rivers, drains, rhymes and ditches.

In the meadows a wide range of plants characteristic of wet grassland can be found, such as Ragged Robin, Marsh Marigold and Meadowsweet. The mires and fen meadows also support less common plants such as Meadow Thistle and Devil's-bit Scabious, food plant for the rare Marsh Fritillary butterfly. Some fields have been agriculturally improved and support a smaller diversity of plants but still provide important feeding areas for grazing wildfowl, notably Bewick's Swan and Wigeon. During the winter, no other inland site in the UK supports as many ducks, swans and waders, including Snipe, Golden Plover and Lapwing some of which occur in flocks of tens of thousands. The area is also well known for breeding waders including Lapwing, Redshank and Curlew. The rivers, rhynes and ditches support a diverse range of plants and invertebrates (described later in this book) and are 'home' to increasing numbers of otters and water voles.

Mute swans.

In recognition of the national nature conservation importance of these Somerset wetlands, approximately 8000 hectares are protected as a series of sixteen Sites of Special Scientific Interest (SSSI) varying in size from 0.5 to over 1000 hectares. Certain habitats are also recognised to be of international importance and 6000 hectares are designated as Special Protection Areas (SPA) under the European Unions Birds Directive and as a Wetland of International Importance (Ramsar Sites).

The key wildlife habitats in the Somerset Levels and Moors are:

International importance: Wet grassland, fen meadows and flood pastures, rivers, ditches and rhynes

National importance: Species-rich hay meadows, wet heath, remnant raised bogs, fen, open water, swamp and reedbed

Regional importance: Wet woodland, withy beds, orchards

Sarah Cross

Storm clouds and flood.

The extraordinary richness of wetlands has been recognised in conservation since the establishment of first nature reserve, Wicken Fen in Cambridgeshire over a century ago. As well as numerous Sites of Special Scientific Interest (SSSI) and county Wildlife Trust sites, the importance of wetlands has been raised again in the recent Biodiversity Action Plans (BAP), with plans for all major types of wetlands. Whilst a wide range of interest is taken into consideration in designating conservation sites, those of most relevance to Somerset's wetlands are wintering wildfowl, breeding waders, aquatic and wetland plants, and aquatic invertebrates.

Vast numbers of over-wintering birds are now recorded on well managed moors such as the RSPB's reserve on West Sedgemoor where peak winter counts of about 80 000 birds have been recorded recently (and how many invertebrates are needed to sustain this abundance?) Bewick's Swan, Teal and Lapwing over-winter here in internationally important numbers, while species on the 'amber' list of threatened birds, such as Widgeon, Shoveler and Pintail, are also present in large numbers. These birds rely on flooded expanses. When this water recedes in spring, leaving saturated ground, a different suite of birds uses the fields for nesting – Snipe, Curlew, Redshank and Lapwing, along with nationally rare Garganey and Black-tailed Godwit. Saturation appears to be essential simply through the mechanics of having to probe with long thin beaks for soil-dwelling invertebrates – a task that becomes increasingly difficult when the surface hardens and the terrestrial grasses form a closed dense mat as the ground dries out.

Willow Man

Willow man created by Serena de la Hey, stands beside the M5 at Bridgwater, welcoming visitors to Sedgemoor.

As she says: 'My work is an exploration of movement through form and structure, conveying traditional working methods and influences in a contemporary way.'

Serena de la Hey

93

About 130 species of the 170 British aquatic plants can be found in ditch systems, and rich examples may have more than 15 species in a 20m section. Each species has its preferred range of water depths in which it flourishes. Most (but not all) submerged species such as the numerous *Potamogeton* species and Water Soldier prefer water deeper than 0.5m, and many (but not all) emergent species that fringe the ditches tolerate just a few centimetres. In general, the wider the range of water depths, the more plants are present.

In contrast, the range of tolerances of wetland plants of the meadows is measured in much smaller differences in wetness. Minor changes in soil wetness or the yearly flooding regime produce major changes in the plant communities, so that small changes in topography allow a wide range of species to thrive. Owing to drier swards tending to be more heavily managed (grazed harder, more fertilizer application) than damper swards, plant communities of wetter sites tend to be more interesting, since only tougher, common plants tend to thrive in the drier areas. Areas that are merely damp on the Levels are often dominated by species-poor Yorkshire-fog or Creeping Bent grass communities, whereas the species-rich flood meadow communities with abundant Meadow Foxtail or Crested Dog's-tail are typical of areas with winter inundation and permanently damp or wet soils. This is a generalisation that does not hold true for unimproved sites with a long history of sympathetic management and low inputs of nutrients, and such grassland can be diverse even though dry all year.

GR

Adult Mayfly (larval stages live in water).

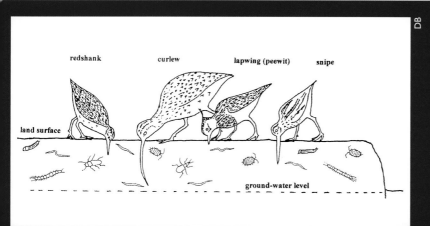

DB

FEEDING STRATEGIES FOR WADING BIRDS

Wading birds have a variety of bill lengths. This enables them to probe for their invertebrate food at differing soil depths and so reduces competition for this resource.

A high ground-water level keeps the bird's food close to the ground surface and lowering this water level by even a few centimetres can put the food out of reach.

In a dry late-spring, chicks may find it difficult to penetrate the earth crust.

Derek Briggs

GR

PHC

Above: Marsh Marigold on West Sedgemoor.

Left: Pollarded willow and ditch near Godney.

Wetland invertebrates on Somerset's wet grasslands, fens and ditches systems are extraordinarily rich. Surveys of such wetlands routinely record hundreds of species in a single year; attempts at complete inventories are perhaps somewhat pointless, if absorbing. More relevant are studies giving us an understanding of their water requirements, which is an aspect that is increasingly well understood for birds and plants but short on evidence for invertebrates.

Issues facing us in holding on to what we have are the amount and quality of the water on these sites. Fierce competition for water leaves wetlands short of supply, when, without abstraction for human consumption, agriculture and industry, they would probably be able to cope with recent droughts. But it is not just the amount of water that causes problems, it is when it arrives. One consequence of global warming is a less reliable timing of rainfall, so warm months get more rain than previously. This can lead to disastrous flooding of fens and marshes, as we have seen in the Somerset Moors in 1997. Breeding waders are displaced, invertebrates capable of surviving winter inundation are killed in a more susceptible phase of their life cycle, and warm water causes massive decay that kills plants, fish and invertebrates.

Greater Westhay NNR.

PHC

Quality of water covers two aspects: its nutrient status and salinity. With the exception of the few remnants of raised bog at Shapwick Heath and Westhay Heath, Somerset has predominantly naturally mesotrophic water supplies, which lead to prolific but diverse vegetation. This richness diminishes when nutrient levels are raised artificially by enrichment from sewage and fertilisers. Insidious increases in nutrients lead to widespread loss of botanical interest, as detailed in the Norfolk grazing marshes where the proportion of aquatic plant communities of high value have dropped dramatically as those dominated by algae and floating duckweed have risen. There are no comparable data for the

THE SHAPWICK GIANT PROJECT

Shapwick Nature Reserve is already well known in the locality, but what Olivia's art project did was to provide a public programme of exciting events from Spring to Autumn. including sheep shearing, an open day, hand felting workshops, making the felt shawl, constructing the Giant sculpture and taking part in the Shapwick Giant Event. During the project large numbers of local people and school children took part and through this, were able to make stronger links with nature and with the reserve. Local people still talk about the giant. Although the location is not widely publicized, friends and relations are eagerly taken to the deep pool where he lies – information of his whereabouts being passed on only by word of mouth.

The Shapwick Giant Project was a great success and made so through the efforts of a talented artist, support from our partners and the enthusiastic participation of local school children. The beautiful felt shawl is preserved and displayed, together with original artwork, poems and stories by the children. The shawl has gone the rounds of other schools and events and could form the basis of many projects as yet un-conceived.

And what have we learnt from the project? That involving communities in big projects is good for us and for English Nature. That art makes no distinction of audience and can make bridges to nature. Oh yes, and that these things tend to grow, now what shall we do next year?

Epilogue:
A conversation overheard on the evening of the Giant Event (5 Sep). A little boy stands beside the Shapwick Giant just before the Giant is to be placed in the deep pool amid piping and chanting from the gathered throng and all around is the still evening sunset:
Boy (Sadly): Where is the giant going?
Adult: Into the water.
Boy: Won't he be lonely?
Adult: No, he has the fish for company.
Boy: Oh
Adult: Stand back now and we'll put him in the water.
Boy: Can I kiss him goodbye?
Adult: Yes
Boy: Goodbye Noah .. Goodbye!

Phil Holms

THE SHAPWICK GIANT'S SHAWL

Noah, a reincarnation using the actual dimensions of fossilised 'giant's bones' dug up from an Irish peat bog in the late 19th century, was constructed by Olivia Keith, Artist in Residence at Shapwick Heath NNR, to be offered to the wetland as a symbol of renewal. He was carried in procession by local school children to his resting place in the water near the Peat Moors Centre on September 5 2004.

A giant is asleep, with his strange felt shawl, swinging on a willow cradle in the large Round House. The giant, Noah, is to be returned this evening, as an offering and symbol of renewal, to the peat bog wetland from whence he came. His contoured body is of coiled reeds, his head of rushes and his legs reed mace. These and the other aromatic plants from which he is made have been harvested from Shapwick Heath Nature Reserve.

The shawl has been felted by local people using fleece from English Nature's flock of Shetland sheep that graze the wild-flower rich pasture on the reserve. The felt was made over several weeks at nearby schools (Meare, Ashcott and Shapwick Manor) and at week-end family workshops. The first took place alongside the sheep being sheared outside the Peat Moors Centre in May this year and depicted the sheep themselves.

Years 5&6 at Meare School based their designs on fragments of Iron Age pottery found at Meare's lake village. Years 3&4 at Ashcott investigated plants from the reserve; their structures, names, medicinal and other uses. The Wildlife Explorers group extended the investigation into plants by experimenting with natural dyes. Shapwick and Edington Schools observed life in the ponds and ditches – 'an otter has left its footprints and the remains of a fish supper!'

The design of each piece of felt reflects the choice of its maker; the individual strips being a personal record of each participant's exploration and relationship with an aspect of Shapwick Heath. Fused together they form the very fabric of the nature reserve; the intersecting histories of people, plants and animals.

Although the giant, especially in his Round House setting, makes obvious references to things past (craft technique, tradition, legend, story-telling) he and his shawl are contemporary constructions made of local sustainable materials, and he is given as a symbol for the future. Both the making of the felt and stitching of Noah involve repetitive and meditative actions; time to contemplate our often estranged relationships with plants, animals and the earth. What are we taking and how are we giving back?

Olivia Keith

THE TALE OF THE SHAPWICK GIANT

The giant of my story has always lived on Shapwick Heath – long, long ago, before the roads and railways and cyclists, long before the Peat Works – before even the peat – in fact as long ago as the time when the heath was completely under water, with only Westhay & Meare Island and the Polden Hills standing out of the flood. And no one had yet named him Noah.

But it soon became clear, once people started to build their trackways over his beautiful wetland wilderness, that the Giant cared as much for the birds, fish, flowers and creeping things that gradually settled here, as for the humans. He showed a healthy contempt for folk who got out of hand and on more than one occasion capsized a dugout canoe and blew a cruel bully off the Sweet Track into the murky waters to drown. Sometimes they tried to placate him by giving him precious offerings; a toy tomahawk, a flint arrowhead and even a polished jadeite axe brought all the way from the Alps.

So later generations came to call him Noah, as they also named a low lying area of the Heath, after Noah who built the ark to save the animals, while people drowned in their selfishness during the Great Flood. The alder trees grew, the eels thrived and the wildfowl flew over Shapwick Heath under Noah's caring and watchful eye.

I first met Noah – well actually I only heard him – this Spring. It was a perfect day with the last of the morning mist melting in the warm air and the first traces of bright green kissing the reeds. To begin with I thought it was just the dry hollow reed stems swelling and clicking together in the sun, but then the voice became clearer…

'Make me into a vessel of reeds and rushes, make my length to be seven-and-a-half cubits and my girth three-and-a-half and give me six toes on my right foot. Make me hollow to provide shelter, make windows of eyes that the fish might enter and nostrils that I may smell the Sweet Gale and make me a mouth that I might murmur, murmur to those with ears to hear. And make me to sleep in a cradle of willow boughs, that I may listen to the sound of the wind in the reeds and the boom of the Bittern when he returns. To return to the place where sky and water meet and fish and fowl and otter dwell.

And that others might share this tale, make with children a woollen shawl, the colour of peat, to tell the story'. And that is what I did.

Olivia Keith

The story of the Shapwick Giant was published in the Polden Post October 2004.

impact of nutrients on invertebrates but limited evidence suggests that ditches dominated by algae and floating duckweed are indeed less species-rich than botanically diverse ditches.

Saline influence can bring either greater interest or a loss. Brackish water is a natural feature of upper saltmarsh and, before sea walls truncated the transition to land, was a natural part of low-lying coasts. As a consequence of its relative scarcity in England, a large proportion of the plants and invertebrates found in this narrow ribbon are uncommon or rare. Less desirable aspects of salinity arise when fresh-water wetlands are occasionally inundated by saline water as a result of exceptional high tides. The effect is to cause local extinction of susceptible species, such as many molluscs and some plants.

The issues of water quality and quantity are large-scale and over-arching. At a more local scale, management has a great influence on the communities of plants and animals. The principal effect of our intervention is to retard or reverse succession to dry land, although this is not what farmers think when they put the cattle out to graze, slub out a ditch or cut reed for thatching. Conservation has taken on these activities for the reason that early successional stages are recognised as having great interest. Land management is therefore a central activity in linking water and wildlife.

The plants of greatest interest in grazing marsh ditches are mainly those of open water, for example many species of *Potamogeton*, and these prosper only when ditches are cleaned out on a fairly frequent cycle of at most a few years. As tall emergent vegetation encroaches from the edges, plant litter accumulates and cattle trample the edges into the ditch, these interesting plants disappear. Relatively few uncommon plants thrive in the late stages when the ditch is choked with a thatch of litter and shaded by the tall emergent monocotyledons. Species-richness also drops as the water becomes shallow so that by the time it is only 0.25m deep, there are very few submerged species left. Fenland management for plants also hinges around maintaining more open conditions by mowing, reed-harvesting or light grazing. Fens left unmanaged usually see a loss of botanical interest, although this is not related to water regime but to the accumulation of plant litter and shading. A different story emerges for invertebrates. Early stages of a ditch support a suite of aquatic invertebrates which includes some real rarities, for example the aquatic soldierfly *Odontomyia ornata*. Because there are many wetland species which rely on saturated conditions rather than deep water, choked ditches have their own set of uncommon species which survive at the water margins, regardless of what happens just a few centimetres into the ditch. As long as the margin remains saturated, or with the shallowest of water, ditches will retain an invertebrate interest. Not surprisingly, these species are typical of fenlands. So, just as the margin of a

PHC

Cottongrass *Eriophorum angustifolium*.

SHAPWICK HEATH – A SPECIAL RESERVE

Shapwick Heath is a major wetland National Nature Reserve (NNR) (400 ha) managed by English Nature, a haven for wildlife and a monument to the history and culture of Neolithic man, who came to this area 6000 years ago and made the moors and marshes his tribal home. The once impenetrable swamplands, abundant with fish and fowl, were accessed by the famous 'Sweet Track' (built in 3806 BC and preserved today), a mammoth task requiring the construction of well over a mile of elevated track way, using hundreds of tons of timber and nothing but simple stone tools.

Much of the watery wilderness of today has been created by restoration of old peat workings. The Romans are thought to be the first to extract the peat for fuel, transporting it on carts or flat-bottomed boats, a technique which continued until the 1950's. The large scale mechanised removal of peat for horticultural use began in the 1960's and ended on Shapwick Heath in the 1990's.

Protected for it's species rich grasslands and mire habitats and forming a key part of the Somerset Levels and Moors Ramsar Site and Special Protection Area (SPA), the wetland areas are internationally important for wintering wildfowl and waders, and support at least 64 species of breeding birds including Lapwing, Grasshopper Warbler, Nightingale, Water Rail, Garganey and upward of 60 pairs of Cetti's Warbler. Bittern are also regular visitors, but have yet to breed. With its complex of ditches and waterways, the site maintains a diverse community of terrestrial and aquatic invertebrates, and thriving populations of both Water Vole and Otter.

Part of the reserve is a traditional farm with organic status, it's pastures and hay meadows managed by annual cutting and grazing with rare breeds of livestock, including Red Devon Cattle and Shetland Sheep. A variety of herb-rich grasslands contain large populations of orchids and other threatened plants. The old farmhouse, now no longer inhabited, has been restored by Vincent Wildlife Trust for use as a 'Bat House and Hibernacula' for its outstanding populations of bat species including Greater and Lesser Horseshoe.

With such an abundance of wildlife, it is easy to see why Shapwick Heath is one of English Nature's high profile 'Spotlight' NNR's attracting over 50,000 visitors a year. Car parks, serviced by way-marked surfaced paths, lead to a series of bird observation hides, some suitable for wheelchairs, and an elevated boardwalk (the 'Discovery Trail') provides a 'close up to nature' experience for disabled visitors. The reserve is used extensively by schools and the local community, a part time Artist-in–Residence runs a series of art workshops as a way to link 'people and nature', and reserve staff provide a busy annual programme of guided walks and public events. Future developments include better visitor access, improved facilities and provision of a local bus service to promote 'green transport'.

Phil J Holms

PHC

ditch may be thought of as a strip of fenland, fens are just extensive water margins. Studies of the invertebrates of East Anglian fens showed that sites with regular mowing or reed harvesting support a less diverse fauna than the unkempt margins or infrequently managed sites. The overall conclusion is that a wide range of hydrological conditions is needed to maintain the invertebrates, although with the underlying need to keep conditions saturated for most of the year.

Thus in conclusion, in both grazing marshes and fens, there is far less need to keep most of the resource at an early hydrological stage in order to maintain both the entomological and botanical interest. There is no doubt that this leads to a minor conflict in interest. However, management for wetland birds on grazing marshes has probably provided a partial resolution since practice on many bird-orientated sites is to provide both open water and broad shallow shelves at the margin of just one ditch. Hydrological succession is thus represented by lateral zonation, rather like that of a pond. It seems likely that a wide range of invertebrate assemblages can be accommodated this way, although I know of no data to prove that this is the case. The only loss of habitat on sites with these broadened ditches with 'battered' margin is some grassland, which is usually of low interest in the context of a wetland fauna unless, as on West Sedgemoor, the grassland is really just a well grazed example of fen.

This article deals with wetlands in the widest sense and has not picked out peatlands for special treatment. Although there are plants and invertebrates that are confined to peatlands but are absent or scarce on alluvium or clay, the general principle remains the same for all soil types. Clean water in good supply in the winter, coupled with management to maintain a wide range of hydrological conditions through the year, is essential to maintain the huge diversity of Somerset's wetlands.

Common Knapweed *Centaurea nigra*.

Wildlife in the Wetlands

David Riley

Living on the Polden Hills on the doorstep of this wild world, I have always felt a privileged onlooker on a countryside that is as diverse in its topography as it is in its Natural History.

We should count ourselves lucky living in Somerset. We are on the edge of some of the wildest places in the British Isles, a sumptuous feast of glittering and exotic wildlife, some of them real celebrities like the Ospreys or 'fish eagles' that drop off at Shapwick Heath en route to Scotland every spring from Spain and North Africa, the Little Egrets that have now taken up permanent residence in our wetlands far from their native Mediterranean marshes or the Nightjars or 'Goatsuckers' with their prehistoric appearance. Few will know that our wetlands are the best place to see Barn Owls. In these open expanses they can quarter the area without danger from busy main roads and food is plentiful - the wetlands are a major stronghold for the Barn Owl in the UK.

These are habitats recognised and envied throughout Europe as arguably the most significant for some species of bird life. For instance, 'Avalon Marshes' comprising several reed bed areas is probably the largest area of wetland reed bed in the whole of Europe. It says little for what we have done to habitats generally but it speaks volumes for the work that is being undertaken in the UK to save our declining wildlife and to put us at the forefront of conservation.

As one countryman reminded me the other day as he introduced me to a secret wooded valley at the back of Ashcott overlooking glistening silver rhynes and smudges of pollarded willows stretching to the horizon, 'this is the Somerset that people don't see - it is the real Somerset that I have loved all my life..;.

Barn Owl. GR

Wintry view of High Ham across the moors from Walton Hill.

And it's true. The holidaymakers and day trippers seem barely distracted by the glimpses of Eden through the gaps in the hedgerows and trees as they make their frenzied dash along the A39 Polden ridge road to join the M5 a little farther along. Away over the tops of the hedgerows there are streaks of silver from the rhynes that criss-cross this wild landscape maintaining the water levels, lagoons the size of reservoirs and in the far distance over the teeming towers and jumbled roofs of a hundred hamlets, the dark bulk of the Mendip hills. Just occasionally huge skeins of Canada Geese will come honking over the ridge road on their way to the next grazing and flocks of piping waders migrating from the north side to the south side. In winter, the lowland moors on either side of the Polden ridge are half drowned in the rain, vast stretches of lagoons ruffled by icy winds, offering very similar habitats to wildlife. Whilst summer days bring a lushness and a cloying humidity - the combination of peat, low levels and lots of lying water creating a 'micro-climate', some 3 or 4 degrees Celsius warmer than on the hills. So 'wetlands' is the generic term for these kindred places.

Barn Owl hunting.

I suppose of all the places where the best views can be had of the 'wetlands' is on Walton Hill. Here there's a crow's nest view of this wilderness landscape. The last time I was there was in early February. It had been a frosty night, an ethereal mist wreathed the levels, only the tops of the trees were visibly floating mysteriously in this transient inland isle. Looking South, to my right, Walton Windmill and to my left and away in the far distance arising out the mist like a stately floating galleon, Dundon Hill and the tree-smothered bluff of the Eastern Poldens overshadowing Compton Dundon. Standing here at any time of day is an experience. Yet first thing in the morning on a cold dawn breathing in the clean air from the wild wetlands beneath is pure pleasure. I watched the sun rise, a fiery orb casting off its misty shroud and gaining prominence until its warming glow illuminated the mist. A commotion of ducks and geese broke the blanketing silence of the mist - Wigeon with their low, soft whistling, the cacophony of Mallard, the joyous calls of Lapwing and the beating of swan wings - sepulchral sounds in this opaque winter world.

Soon the wooded valley lying at the bottom of the hill emerged from the mist ringing out with the awakening songs of birds - a Mistle Thrush, a song that pealed like Sunday church bells through the valley, then Robins, Blackbirds, Song Thrushes, Great Tits and Hedge Sparrows - Buzzards mewing and the stentorian croaks of Ravens flying along the escarpment. There was the loud clamour from a rookery somewhere down in the valley amongst the Oak, Ash and Birch. A Great Spotted Woodpecker was drumming close by and the neurotic shriek of a Green Woodpecker echoed along the face of the hill.

The mist was soon burnt off and hung like rolls of dirty washing on the distant horizons. For as far as the eye could see runnels of water opening up into wider lagoons with flickering colours and movement from hundreds, perhaps thousands, of ducks and geese – the white smudges of swans and huge flocks of Lapwing like wisps of smoke rising and falling over this sunken landscape. The patterned land with its 'droves' slightly raised, in defiance of the submerged world lapping at their foundations, occasional towers peering out of the mist beyond the turgid, peat brown crawl of the King's Drain. Real Somerset.

On the other side, the North side of the Poldens is Catcott Heath and Catcott Lows Nature Reserve. You can reach the hide at Catcott Lows by car or foot alongside the Broad Drove. In winter this large expanse of water is bristling with waders and ducks. I visited in the first week of February on a day of driving rain and stinging hail. Even before I'd entered the warmth and dry of the hide at least 60 handsome male Shoveler ducks could be counted amongst what must have been approaching a 1000 Wigeon and some Teal. Once in the hide there is a community of kindred spirit – we discuss recent observations - cross check sightings and make references to birds seen in the hide 'record' book. For the entire period of the time I was in the hide a Merlin stood sentinel on a half sunken post. In the pelting rain it seemed a permanent fixture quite unaware of the binoculars and 'scopes' trained on it. In the Alders fringing the lagoon two Sparrow Hawks could just be spotted.

I could see Pintail duck – not diving but up-turned, their long tails a precise giveaway. One or two Common Pochard. Earlier Greylag Geese, Bean and Pink-footed Geese, Golden Plover, Snipe and Redshank had been seen.

But of all the birds I saw on that wet afternoon the sight of thousands of Lapwings (Peewit or Green Plovers) coming in to land as the light faded was uplifting. More kept coming, in the far distance long,

GR

Whitethroat on *Phragmites*.

Lapwing.

tapering, shimmering streamers of birds enfolding the horizon in a kind of pincer movement then descending with all the noise and clamour you could imagine. Such a lovely sight, it made my heart skip - as they rolled and wheeled above the watercovered land until it seemed the whole marsh was throbbing with their joyous cries.

I walked back along the drove with the cries of the Lapwings still ringing in my head – call me senti-mental but this is heaven on earth. And as I returned to the parked car, Long-tailed Tits, Goldcrests and Coal Tits were fussing about in the Alders and Birch that fringe the drove on both sides.

On the other side of Catcott Lows is Catcott Heath. You approach it on foot by way of an arbour of Alders; a beguiling path that runs alongside lush meadows on one side and the dark, damp depth of the 'carr' woodland on the other.

Roe Deer.

GR

When I last visited it was early autumn. Half submerged in the meadow grass was a group of Roe Deer grazing unconcernedly. I was a privileged onlooker, watching their private and secret lives from a distance; one a fawn, the others adults with a male displaying small truncated antlers. I crouched gazing at the peaceful scene, luxuriating in the sensation that I was alone, detached from the world and its problems. Suddenly, from behind, a Great Spotted Woodpecker with post office red flanks scolded loudly. Ears pricked and from that moment on the deer were alert to my quiet vigil. Despite crouching motionless they seemed to know instinctively where I was - they looked straight in my direction through the latticework of leafy branches. I'd been rumbled.

You normally see Roe Deer splashing through the flooded fields on winter days when cover is at a premium and they rely more on turn of speed than camouflage.

The 'carr' woodland is on a peat base with Alder, Willow and Birch the principal trees all jostling for space and light. It's a bewitching place. On the day I last visited, Willow Tits, Coal Tits and Long-Tailed Tits busied themselves hoovering up the aphids amongst the Alders. The peat diggings are home to Great Crested and Smooth Newts. On this autumn day the wildflowers that grow in abundance in the summer, were few in number, Purple Loosestrife, Hemp Agrimony, Devil's Bit Scabious, Meadowsweet, Common Mallow and the huge tropical fronds of the Royal Fern. In the summer some of the UK's rarest wildflowers can be seen such as Sundew, Bog Bean and Marsh Pea. And there are over 60 different kinds of fungi. It's all a humbling experience – it makes you realise how little most of us know about about the growing things that share our environment. Catcott Heath has several bird hides, one of these is constructed out of willow hurdles and in memory of 'John Langridge'. John must have held the key to a magic world because the hide named after him looks out to a wetland field where Swallows were skimming and Chiffchaffs, Blackcaps and Willow Warblers were calling. A Short-eared Owl was hunting low along the edge of the field calling 'keow-keow'. I could hear the constant barracking from ducks in the nearby reed-bed. Shapwick Heath nature reserve sits alongside Catcott Heath - a seamless patchwork of wetland reserves. From the hide I could make out the gaunt, witch-like shapes of Cormorants perching on the half submerged dead trees in one of the lagoons. They struck an heraldic pose with outstretched wings drip-drying in the afternoon sun.

Everyone living in the Polden villages, north or south of the ridge road has seen the streaming flocks of Starlings heading north over the hills on late winter afternoons. There is an intent and

A MURMURATION OF STARLINGS

One... two... three... four...
A hundred...a thousand...
Maybe more.
They fill the skies.
They fill your *eyes,*
Descending down
Like swarms of flies.
One thousand...
Two thousand...
Three thousand.. .four;
A million starlings,
Maybe more.

Where do *they* come from?
How do *they* know
Which one is their leader?
Which way to go?
A continuous ribbon
Entwined in the clouds;
A swirling tornado...
A heavenly shroud.
One million... Two million...
Three million..four...
A zillion starlings.
From heaven do pour.

To rest on the reed-bed
From dusk to dawn,
Then rise with the sun
As a new day is borne.
One million...
Two million...
Three million...four;
A Murmuration of starlings
to heaven do so

Lynne Newton

determination that echoes back through the centuries. Generations of Starlings have looked down upon the villages as they have made this pilgrimage over countless years.

With Starling numbers declining and those big, noisy city roosts almost a spectacle of the past it is refreshing to have one of the largest Starling megalopolis in the south of England at the Westhay Nature Reserve some two or three miles North of the Poldens.

Two million birds, swollen by continental Starlings, roost at Westhay every late autumn and winter. Once and not so long ago, numbers exceeded 4 million. They come to Westhay Nature Reserve for warmth and protection from winter's blasts. Clinging to the reed stems like alien black fruits they spend long, dark nights in this social, well ordered society.

I've seen this sight on numerous occasions - not always presenting the same breathtaking spectacle. One visit stands out. It was early December. The temperature had barely risen above freezing all day and the deepest of cloudless blue skies with desultory winter sunshine foretold a glorious sunset and a hard overnight frost.

Starlings come in from all points of the compass in their thousands to Westhay North from the Mendips, from Bridgwater, from the Poldens, the Levels and the Moors. They begin this journey in mid winter at around 3pm. Having been feeding in the wetlands on worms and invertebrates they assemble thickly on overhead power cables or awkwardly line the 'stays' of electricity posts like black rime. Then, some unseen signal tells them the moment has arrived to start the journey to Westhay. I've seen huge gatherings in Stawell and Chedzoy near Bridgwater, filling the trees one moment then gone the next. This telepathy carries them in vast amorphous flocks, choreographed to a fine art, swirling and eddying as though swept hither and thither by unseen winds.

So standing in the hide at Westhay alongside the main drove at around 3.30p.m. on a cold winter's afternoon I watched one of Somerset's best Natural dramas being played out. For an hour mesmerising clouds of Starlings came flying in. Some flew straight and fast over the hide with a sudden rush of air whilst others swept in on never ending tides that stretched a good mile. The flocks seemed to turn in on themselves as though engineered by digital technology then, just as quickly, levelled out followed by a perceptible upward flip before being sucked into the reed vortex with only the constant chatter to identify their presence. And still they came, sleeting in across this lonely

Opposite page: Starling. TR

landscape, groups melting into large thick black wedges that wheeled and twisted before plunging into the reeds. No matter how many more large flocks arrived there seemed limitless bed and breakfast accommodation in this horizon-less landscape.

Words are empty when describing this Starling spectacle - it has to be one of the most awe-inspiring movements of bird life in the World - an 8th wonder! I implore everyone to go and witness the winter drama at Westhay - it has to be seen and heard to be believed, to fully appreciate the sheer volume of chatter turned up to full by millions of conversing Starlings. The Starlings' chatter sounded like high-pitched static on a radio - if I hadn't just observed two million birds settle for the night I would have mistaken the sound for some top secret military hardware.

But danger lurks over these reed-bed landscapes. In winter the Peregrine Falcons see thousands of roost-bound Starlings as easy pickings. I saw one bringing up the rear searching out a straggler whilst during the height of summer, the Hobbys from the Mediterranean sweep and stoop on the hapless Swallows and Martins

It was a scene of indescribable peace and sheer beauty. As the light faded, dulling the red ribbons of a sunset, I just stood alone in the hide listening to the sounds of a reed-bed flooded by the milk white light from a full moon - a vast featureless landscape that seemed to lap the very foot-hills of the Mendips several miles away. From across the empty miles Tawny Owls hooted and Little Owls shouted. Water Rails squealed like frightened piglets. Cetti's Warblers were still singing after dusk and just occasionally I glimpsed the ungainly silhouettes of Cormorants settling in the reed bed. Herons croaked, Wigeon whistled softly and from somewhere in the enveloping black Canada Geese honked loudly. Overhead I heard the thin 'seep' of Redwings and the chuckles of Fieldfares - Viking invaders down from Scandinavia for another winter.

As I looked back over the endless miles of reeds towards the enormous dark bulk of the Mendips, the lights of little hamlets and cottages snuggling in the folds of the hills winked - a slight breeze rushed through the reeds and that deep sigh seemed in step with this beautiful, peaceful landscape. You can't get enough of these places, the soothing silence, the call of the wild. For me the desperate desire is to contribute to preserving it for future generations so that they will experience the magic of these wetlands.

Wetland Plants – Sink or swim?

Stephanie Greshon & Katherine Emms

Ditches are wetland habitats that support an interesting variety of aquatic plants, including floating, emergent and submerged species. Some reflect the historic ecological changes that have taken place, others have been introduced more recently as man left his mark on the land. As the name suggests, floating aquatic plants literally float on the surface of the water with their roots either hanging into the water or anchored in the sediment at the bottom of the ditch. The most common plants in this group are the duckweeds *Lemna* species (spp) which can cover the entire surface water of a ditch with their dense, free-floating vegetation and prevent light reached submerged plants below. Frog-bit *Hydrocharis morsus-ranae* is another floating aquatic plant frequently found in the ditches of the Somerset Levels and Moors.

Emergent aquatic plants, which root in the ditch bottom but have aerial leaves and flowers, are exemplified in the Somerset Levels and Moors by water plantains *Alisma* spp., the distinctive Arrowhead *Sagittaria sagittifolia*, Flowering Rush *Butomus umbellatus* and bur-reeds *Sparganium* spp.. Other species include the Lesser Water Parsnip *Berula erecta*, Fool's Watercress *Apium nodiflorum*, Greater Water Parsnip *Sium latifolium* and Watercress *Rorippa nasturtium-aquaticum*.

Pondweeds *Potamogeton* spp. and starworts *Callitriche* spp. are examples of submerged aquatic plants, usually anchored to the ditch bottom. Some species of pondweed and starwort also have floating leaves, which are morphologically different from those that are submerged. Other submerged aquatic plant species include Canadian Waterweed *Elodea canadensis*, Opposite-leaved Pondweed *Groenlandia densa*, Nuttall's Waterweed *Elodea nuttallii* and the water crowfoots *Ranunculus* spp.. The Water Violet *Hottonia palustris* has delicate, violet-like aerial flowers but the rest of the plant is submerged. Bladderworts *Utricularia* spp. are insectivorous aquatic plants with a complex trap mechanism for capturing prey and, like Water Violet, raise their striking yellow flowers above the water for

GR

DB

Yellow (Flag) Iris *pseudacorus*.

pollination. Insectivorous plants are found where the nutrient content of the soil or water is very low, they therefore need an alternative source of proteins, in this case the insects that get trapped and subsequently digested by the plant.

Aquatic plants are very specialised and have a number of adaptations to the environment in which they live. The submerged species in particular, have little strengthening tissue which means they 'flop' when taken out of the water. Floating leaves are an adaptation which allows plants to obtain as much sunlight as possible by spreading out over the surface of the water and creating a large surface area with which to absorb sunlight. The leaves are able to float because they contain lots of air spaces that increase buoyancy. Unlike terrestrial plants, which generally have pores, called stomata, on the underside of their leaves, floating leaves have stomata on their upper surface so they are in contact with the atmosphere rather than the water. A waxy or hairy waterproof coating on the surface of the leaves keeps water out of the stomata for efficient gas exchange. It also repels water so they do not become swamped if the water surface is disturbed. A good example of a hairy, non-wetting plant is the Water Fern *Azolla filiculoides*. Its beauty, the colour and the hairs, is best seen under a microscope.

Floating aquatic plants are at risk of becoming frozen into a surface layer of ice if the water in the ditch in which they live freezes over in winter. However, some small floating aquatic plants have evolved a clever mechanism for avoiding such a fate. Duckweeds and Frog-bit build up starch in their cells at the surface of the water. This alters their chemistry and causes either the whole plant or regenerative parts of the plant to sink to the bottom of the ditch and remain dormant over winter. These over-wintering buds are known as turions. Although many of the plants may die, some survive and a springtime increase in water temperature causes the starch to be broken down. The energy released is used by the plant in growth, reducing the density of the plants so they float back up to the surface where they can continue growing.

The height that emergent plants grow to (often a metre or more) is an adaptation that allows the plants to grow taller than the surrounding vegetation so they are not over-shadowed and can access light needed for photosynthesis. Being tall also means that the plants can withstand seasonal fluctuations in water levels and even during flooding part of the leaf is always above the water level. Their leaves are strong but flexible, which increases resistance to possible damage by high winds. There are large air spaces in the long leaves and stems that allow oxygen to be transferred from aerial parts of the plant to the underwater regions.

Unbranched Bur-reed *Sparganium emersum*.

Frogbit *Hydrocharis morsus-ranae*.

Arrowhead *Sagittaria sagittifolia*.

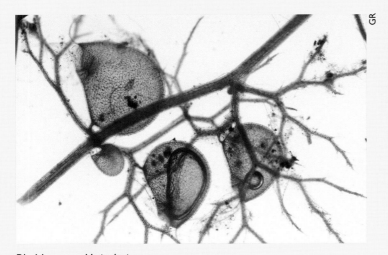

Bladderwort *Utricularia* sp.

Water Violet *Hottonia palustris*.

DIAGRAMS SHOWING THE VARIOUS STAGES OF NATURAL SUCCESSION, FROM OPEN WATER TO WOODLAND, IN A TYPICAL LEVELS DITCH

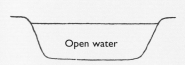

Stage 1.
Profile through newly cleaned ditch, an open community.

Stage 2.
Invasion of the ditch by aquatic plants and by plants from the banks.

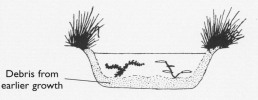

Debris from earlier growth

Stage 3.
The ditch becomes narrower and shallower.

Raised floor of ditch

Stage 4.
The ditch is almost completely 'filled-in' and very little open water is left for the few remaining aquatic plants.

Stage 5.
The site of the ditch is filled with marsh plants and young carr is becoming established.

Stage 6.
The marsh plants are suppressed by the carr and, if grazing is prohibited, a further rise in ground level can occur due to the dead leaves, etc from the overhanging trees.

Finally the alder- birch- willow carr is replaced by true woodland trees. This is the climax stage.

Drawings from Storer's *Natural History of the Somerset Levels*

In contrast to terrestrial plants, submerged aquatic plants are not at risk of drying out due to water loss through their stomata. In fact, they don't have any stomata. They have a very limited waxy coating on their leaves as it is not required to prevent desiccation, and gases associated with photosynthesis and respiration diffuse directly into and out of the cells from and into the surrounding water. The leaf dimorphism displayed by some pondweeds and starwort is an adaptation that allows the plant to carry out photosynthesis both in and out of the water. The aerial leaves are inefficient for photosynthesis if submerged, but the underwater leaves show adaptations to underwater life through their shape. Some submerged aquatic plants are characterised by having highly dissected (divided) leaves and stems which increases the surface area available for the absorption of light and diffusion of gases.

DB

Amber snail *Succinea putris* and large red Damselfly *Pyrrhosoma nymphula*.

Aquatic plants are able to regenerate rapidly after being damaged or to colonise a new area through vegetative reproduction. This is a useful adaptation to aquatic life where currents or changes in water level may cause stems to break off, or particularly in the ditch habitat, trampling by livestock may occur. Flowering aquatic plants can also reproduce by producing seeds and these show adaptations to aquatic life through their ability to float.

Green plants form the basis of food chains in any ecosystem through their role as primary producers. Through the process of photosynthesis they use the Sun's energy to make organic molecules (carbohydrates) from simple inorganic molecules (water and carbon dioxide). This energy is then passed to herbivores that eat the plants and subsequently predators that eat the herbivores. Although simple food chains involving a single species at each level can be described, the complex transfer of energy within an ecosystem is better described using a food web, which involves several species of producer, herbivore and predator at each level.

Oxygen produced through photosynthesis dissolves in the water of the ditch and becomes available to other organisms for respiration. Simpler animals, for example worms and leeches, are able to absorb oxygen through their body surface, but higher animals such as fish and insect larvae, obtain oxygen dissolved in the water through their specially adapted gills. In waters polluted with a lot of organic matter (for example ditches bordering farmland where organic fertilisers are used) there will be a large number of bacteria present, using up the oxygen in the water in their respiration. The amount of oxygen removed by the bacteria is known as the biochemical oxygen demand (BOD) and it is a measure of how polluted a body of water is. A high BOD means a reduced amount of oxygen available for other organisms. High numbers of bacteria can also cause problems in an aquatic ecosystem by increasing turbidity in the water and thus reducing light available to plants for photosynthesis. Plants play an important role in reducing the BOD and turbidity and thereby ameliorating the habitat in general.

Aquatic plants of the ditches also provide shelter and protection for animals, provide shading from direct sun and heat and provide breeding sites for a number of invertebrates, such as dragonflies. Early on warm sunny mornings, dragonfly larvae in their final instar or moult will crawl up the stems of emergent aquatic plants such as sedges and rushes and make their final transformation into the adult insects. They leave behind the light brown papery cases stuck to the stems as the only sign of their previous existence as aquatic ditch dwellers. Water snails will lay their jelly-like eggs on the leaves of submerged plants and for many aquatic invertebrates these plants provide safe hiding places from predators

Like any ecosystem, if left undisturbed, ditches undergo ecological succession. This is a process whereby the different species making up a community are replaced by other species over time, from a pioneer community (the first organisms to colonise an area) to a climax community (organisms present in the final stage of succession). In the case of ditch plant communities, succession is relatively rapid and results in a gradual change from open water to dry land in as little as four to six years.

The pioneer community in a newly created ditch or newly cleaned ditch consists of floating plants which colonise the open water. They may be washed in from connected ditches or get into the ditch on the feet of livestock. Species diversity within the ditch ecosystem increases as the submerged aquatic plants begin to become established. Throughout the growing season these plants increase in mass until the winter months when many die. The remains of dead plants sink to the bottom of the ditch where they decay. A build up of decaying matter on the ditch bottom causes the ditch to become shallower and therefore suitable for the colonisation of the emergent species. The cycle of growth and decay gradually continues to make the ditch shallower and the growth of emergent plants at the edges of the ditches encroaches on the open water and makes them narrower.

As the amount of open water available to aquatic plants decreases, fewer aquatic plants can survive, as they are out-competed by marsh plants. The ground in higher areas will gradually dry out and firm up, eventually becoming unsuitable for marsh plants so the community gives way to other non-aquatic plant species and finally shrubs and trees such as ash, oak and birch. However, in low-lying areas, the ground will remain wet and give rise to wet woodland with willow and alder. The introduction of

Opposite page:
Shapwick sunset LN

grazing over much of the Somerset Levels and Moors has meant that tree saplings are unable to grow and grassland and pasture tends to form the end point of the succession.

In order to prevent the accumulation of organic matter, and therefore control the natural succession towards dry land, ditches are intermittently cleared or dredged. The establishment of emergents normally marks the turning point in the ditch cycle, so it is at this point that ditches are normally cleared out.

It can take several years for a ditch to reach its maximum plant species diversity (longer for animals, especially those found in late-succession ditches) so traditional forms of management where the ditches were cleaned by hand periodically enabled the distinct communities associated with the different stages of ditch succession to thrive.   However, the introduction of more frequent mechanical management of ditches as farming became more intensified has led to the loss of some of the more diverse middle-aged ditches and entire communities can be destroyed due to insensitive management.   The most species rich ditches now tend to be in the protected Nature Reserves on the Somerset Levels and Moors where traditional management techniques can be maintained.

The aim of management techniques, targeted at maintaining the nature conservation value of ditches, is to provide the best possible ditch habitat to support the highest diversity of plant and animal species. This means a range of aquatic plants to provide food for herbivores, and shelter, foraging and breeding sites for ditch fauna, with sufficient light available to plants for photosynthesis but not so much as to encourage blanket growth of floating plants.   Mechanical clearing should generally not be carried out more than once every five years.   Only one side of a ditch should be cleared at any one time, or only short lengths, which allows some plants to survive and re-colonise cleared areas.   Hand raking is a preferred method for clearing, since it allows animals to drop back into the water as the plant material is lifted out.   Clearing should involve removing plants only from the banks, to avoid damage to pupating beetles.   Banks should be kept gently sloping to allow the migration of animal species into and out of the ditch.

The importance of the ditches of the Somerset Levels and Moors in terms of their biodiversity value should not be underestimated.   They represent a highly specialised aquatic habitat harbouring rare plants and animals, many of which have their stronghold of distribution centred on the Somerset Levels and Moors.   Their continued survival will ensure that these ecosystems continue to thrive and will provide enjoyment, education and research potential for future generations.

Clingers, Crawlers and Swimmers – Going with the flow

Pat Hill-Cottingham

The waterways on the Levels and Moors form an intricate, interconnecting network of rivers and man-made ditches of all sizes. It is by no means a 'natural' environment, but, with its variety of wildlife, it is of endless interest and fascination. The lowland meadows and droves, with the occasional copse, add to the patchwork of gently meandering rivers (except when in spate after heavy rain) and slow-flowing drains, rhynes and ditches. The rate of flow of the water not only depends on the slope of the land but also the amount of vegetation present. Ditches pass through the various stages of vegetational succession within 3-5 years, becoming more and more clogged with a wide range of emergent plants. In contrast, to survive in faster flowing water, plants need a foothold by anchoring to the bottom. There are fewer species of these, for example the water buttercups, and they rarely block the channel.

Aquatic animals have developed strategies to cope with water flow and we can call them clingers, crawlers or swimmers. The range of species can vary quite considerably in number and type, in waterways with different rates of flow. We can thus pick out 'typical' species associated with Somerset ditches. For example, there are just nine species of aquatic beetle to be found on all the recorded Somerset Moors and that have been recorded in all environmental surveys to date. These are *Agabus bipustulatus, Anacaena limbata, Helophorus brevipalpis, Hydaticus transversalis, Hydrobius fuscipes, Hydroporus palustris, Hygrotus inaequalis, Hyphydrus ovatus* and *Rhantus frontalis*. Of these, *H. transversalis* RDB3 and *R. frontalis* Nb are classified as notable species. Similarly the typical mollusc species are: *Anisus vortex, Bathyomphalus contortus, Lymnaea palustris, Lymnaea peregra, Planorbis planorbis*. A range of insect larvae and crustaceans are found commonly but not necessarily in every ditch.

GR

BOTH PHOTOGRAPHS PHC

Above left: River Brue – a slow-flowing river.

Above right: A faster flowing river creates turbulence and absorbs more oxygen.

River Limpet *Ancylus fluviatilis*.

The commonest freshwater shrimp in ditches is *Crangonyx pseudogracilis*, in rivers this species is replaced by *Gammarus pulex*.

Imagine trying to maintain one's position in fast flowing water – one either has to be a very strong swimmer or be able to cling to the underside of stones or on to the plants to prevent being swept away. In slow flowing water this risk is low, so one finds all three categories of adaptation present. On the other hand, slow flowing water contains less dissolved oxygen than in turbulent, fast lowing water and animals in ditches therefore show various ingenious ways of getting enough oxygen – the commonest being coming up for air!

Clingers achieve their objective in two main ways, by means of suction or by flattening the body so that it offers less resistance to the flow. The freshwater limpets River Limpet *Ancylus fluviatilis* and Lake Limpet *Acxroloxus lacustris* have conical shells held flat to the surface of stones by the broad foot. They are found only in rivers with a suitable stony substrate – lift up a stone in a more sheltered shallow and you can find limpets sticking to the under-surface. They can crawl slowly, grazing on

Food web in a Catcott ditch.

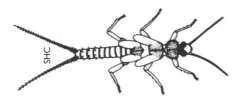

Stonefly *Trichoptera*.

Mayfly *Ephemeroptera*.

Larva of *Dytiscus* beetle.

Caddis larva.

algae. The leeches are supplied with a sucker at each end of the body. As they move they detach one sucker at a time, extending or contracting the body to change position. The oral sucker, around the mouth, also enables them to cling to the body of another animal, perhaps a fish or insect larva, to suck its blood for food. Leeches are found in all types of water body, but some species such as the Fish Leech *Pisicola geometra* prefer faster flowing water.

Examples of clingers with flattened body shape include the larvae of several species of stonefly Trichoptera and mayfly Ephemeroptera. One of the more common mayflies is the genus *Ecdyonurus*. These have short flat bodies and broad flat legs with claws at the end so that they can cling to the under side of stones. They swim in a rather sluggish undulating manner amongst the crevices in quieter stretches of a river to feed on detritus. Some of the caddis fly larvae live permanently in cases glued to the underside of stones – they just stick their heads, armed with large biting mandibles, out of the end of the case to grab any passing prey.

Ditches have lots of crawlers – insect larvae, snails, water-louse, and bugs. Legs are often clawed to get a grip; longer-legged ones can be found on the surface where they won't get tangled up – pond skaters, for example. A great many insects, beetles, flies, caddis flies, mayflies, stoneflies, alder flies, dragonflies and damselflies, for example, have an aquatic larval stage in their life cycle. Sometimes this is the dominant phase, there are species of caddis and dragonfly which live up to three years as larvae and metamorphose into adults for one season, solely to lay the next generation of eggs. As a result, there is a great complex web of prey and predators, all dependent ultimately on the submerged, floating and emergent plants.

The swimmers include many beetles, water boatmen and, of course, fish. Good swimmers amongst the beetles and water boatmen have broad paddle-shaped legs with long fringing hairs for good propulsion. The fish have streamlined bodies, offering less resistance to water flow, and include sticklebacks, roach, trout and gobies. One can always tell a swift swimmer by the elongated body shape and the narrow tail in front of the tail fin; the Three-spined Stickleback *Gasterosteus aculeatus* and Ten-spined Stickleback *Pungitius pungitius* are good examples. The sticklebacks are extremely important in the ditches, they eat a vast number of mosquito larvae and pupae! More sluggishly swimming fish have a broader end to

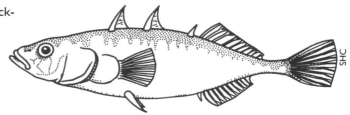

Three-spined Stickleback *Gasterosteus aculeatus*.

the body immediately in front of the tail fin and are less sleek in shape with larger pectoral fins. Often, as in the Bullhead *Cottus gobio*, the underside is wider than the topside – enabling them to hug the substrate to avoid being swept away.

One can still find crawlers such as Water Louse *Asellus aquaticus* and freshwater shrimps such as *Gammarus pulex* in a river but they tend to be amongst the bottom debris in shallower areas where they can feed on the organic detritus. The Water Louse *Asellus aquaticus* is found in all ditches but the other species *A. meridianus* is becoming progressively rarer. It can still be found in a few ponds on Pawlett Hams.

Molluscs are far more common in slow flowing or still water bodies. In Sites of Special Scientific Interest (SSSIs) as many as 20 species of gastropod and bivalve molluscs can be found in the waterways. In general the larger species, freshwater mussels such as the Swan Mussel *Anodonta cygnaea*, the Duck Mussel *Anodonta anatin,* the rare Compressed River Mussel *Pseudanodonta complanata* and

The water louse is a crawling scavenger.

Terrestrial adult Cadis.

Leeches can cling with suckers at each end of the body.

125

WHO EATS WHOM ON STREET HEATH

CARNIVOROUS PLANTS

Street Heath has had two species of sundew, two species of bladderwort and Pale Butterwort over the years. The protein in their diet provides the nitrates lacking in bog water.

Sundew has trapped some flies
Drosera intermedia with unidentified *Diptera*.

Sundews have caught a dragonfly
Round-leaved and Oblong-leaved Sundews *Drosera rotundifolia* and *D. intermedia* with a female Black-tailed Skimmer *Orthetrum cancellatum*, the largest prey observed.

DRAGONFLIES AS PREDATORS

Dragonfly eats dragonfly
A male Emperor Dragonfly *Anax imperator* has caught a Four-spotted Chaser *Libellula quadrimaculata*.

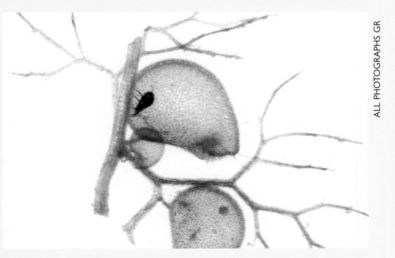

Bladderwort has trapped a mite
Utricularia sp. (*U. minor* and *U. australis* have flowered at Street Heath).

SPIDERS AS PREDATORS

Spider eats bush-cricket
The Raft Spider Dolomedes fimbriatus has captured a Bog Bush-cricket *Metrioptera brachyptera* which probably jumped into the pool.

Spider eats leaf-hopper
Unidentified spider and *Cicadella viridis*.

Spider eats butterfly
The crab spider *Misumena* vatia making a small contribution to the extinction of the Marsh Fritillary *Eurodryas (Euphydryas) aurinia* at Street Heath.

Spider eats dragonfly
The Raft Spider *Dolomedes fimbriatus* has taken a Common Darter *Sympetrum striolatum*. The spider, which can walk on water, uses the surface as a web. It feels vibrations from the prey and pounces; the dragonfly may have been laying eggs in the water.

Barn owl.

Barn Owl nest box on a pole on Shapwick.

DEATH ON SILENT WINGS – THE DIET OF A BARN OWL

Owls and some other birds regurgitate the indigestible parts of their food as pellets, consisting of fur and bones. A series of barn owl pellets from Sharpham Moor Plot in March 2000 contained short-tailed field vole as the main component. Skulls or jaws of the following species indicated a varied diet and an interesting small mammal population in the area; Water Vole, Field Mouse, Harvest Mouse, Water Shrew, Common Shrew, Pygmy Shrew, young Brown Rat and Starling.

Dissected owl pellet.

Four-spotted Chaser *Libellula quadrimaculata.*

PHC

the *Unio* species – Painter's Mussel *U. pictorum* and the more solid and heavy *U. tumidus* can all be found in the rivers. The two latter species have strong teeth in the hinge of the shell, locking the valves together; whereas, in the former three, the shell valves are held together by the ligament only. There are also very small bivalves, the orb and pea mussels, in ditches, the commonest is the orb mussel *Sphaerium corneum*. The larger gastropods, the viviparous river snails *Viviparus viviparus*, and, less commonly, *Viviparus contectus*, can be found in the drains and larger rhynes. These fall prey to Herons, I once saw the remains of dozens of River Snails on the banks of the Black Ditch with neat holes where Herons had pierced the shell for the meat.

The bivalve molluscs are all filter feeders, sitting on the bottom with the valves apart drawing in a current of water over the gills, sifting our particles of food, and passing the water out at the other end. The very small pea and orb mussels have inhalent and exhalent siphons through which water and food particles pass.

All the other water snails are vegetarian, browsing on the submerged water plants. They especially favour Ivy-leaved Duckweed *Lemna trisulca*, a species which is submerged a few centimetres below the surface, delivering oxygen directly into the water, and which is much more succulent than the floating duckweeds. *Lemna trisulca* is probably the most important submerged plant in Somerset's ditches – where it is present, there is found the greatest diversity of animal life. It is a plant which simply floats in the water and so has no defence against swift flowing water and is not found in rivers.

Evolution over the millennia has brought about an incredible diversity of adaptations to the aquatic life-style and the ditches in Somerset are one of our most species-rich habitats. They need to be treated sympathetically; however, the animal life within them takes at least ten years to reach full succession and too frequent cleaning sets back the process. We have to compromise between the use of ditches as stock-proof 'wet fences' and as late succession wildlife habitats – this is possible with careful management, maintaining more open ditches for inflow and outflow and to keep in stock, but with internal ditches left to develop for a longer period of time where their use as a barrier is not essential. Dipping a net into a ditch to see what is there is great fun – try it! But do make sure you return the animals, unharmed, to their habitat.

Ditch with Yellow Iris
(Flag) *Iris pseudacorus.*

SHC

Great Pond Snail *Lymnaea stagnalis.*

Ecology and Conservation of the Lesser Silver Water Beetle *Hydrochara caraboides* on the Somerset Levels

David Boyce

The Lesser Silver Water Beetle is currently known from only two areas in Britain. The first of these is on the Cheshire Plain, where it occurs in field ponds in both Cheshire, and across the Welsh border into Denbighshire. However, the largest British population is on the Somerset Levels, where it is restricted to the peat-moors of the Brue valley. During the current study, most records of this species have come from Shapwick Heath National Nature Reserve (NNR), and this site supports the largest colonies of *Hydrochara* in Somerset. Other breeding sites for the species have been discovered at Westhay Moor NNR, Ham Wall NNR and Westhay Heath, and adults were also recorded at Catcott Heath, Tadham Moor and Catcott Grounds. Historically the Lesser Silver Water Beetle had a wider distribution that also included the East Anglian fens, the marshes around London and Askham Bog in Yorkshire. It had disappeared from all of these other areas by the early twentieth century, and until its discovery in Cheshire in 1990, it was for many years thought to be confined in Britain to the Somerset Levels.

Because of its extreme rarity, and the decline in its British range, the Lesser Silver Water Beetle is protected under Schedule 5 of the Wildlife and Countryside Act, which prohibits collecting of all stages of the species. It is listed in the British Red Data Book (RDB) as Red Data Book 1 (Endangered) and is a priority species in the UK Biodiversity Action Plan (BAP). The BAP includes a set of objectives and actions for the beetle that aim to maintain and enhance its British populations. English Nature is charged with delivering the objectives laid out in the BAP and the work carried out in this project aims to meet these objectives.

Egg cocoon – note the aerial mast.

Larva.

MANAGEMENT FOR THE LESSER SILVER DIVING BEETLE

It is fortunate that the main breeding colonies of *Hydrochara caraboides* are on land owned and managed by conservation organisations (Shapwick Heath NNR by English Nature, Westhay Moor NNR by the Somerset Wildlife Trust and Ham Wall NNR by the Royal Society for the Protection of Birds). Bearing in mind the habitat requirements set out in the article, the following management recommendations are suggested.

• Ensure that the ditch clearing rotation allows for the development of late-successional ditches with shallow water and thick bottom sediments.

• Maintain at least partial tree cover along late-successional ditches within breeding areas.

• Manage water levels to ensure that there is suitable shallow water (less than one metre) within breeding areas from March through to July.

• Maintain areas of seasonally flooded swamp woodland within the Somerset peat moors. Create new areas of habitat by raising water levels in wet woodland between March and July.

• Avoid clearance of ditches within breeding areas between May and August inclusive, when egg cocoons and larvae are in the water, or when pupae are present in ditch banks.

• Investigate techniques for controlling the growth of duckweed within areas that would otherwise provide suitable breeding habitat for *Hydrochara*. Monitor the results of any experimental *Lemna* control in allowing colonisation by breeding lesser silver water-beetle.

David Boyce

ALL PHOTOGRAPHS CJM WALTERS

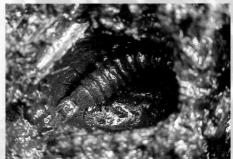

Pre-pupa.

Adult beetle.

Larva feeding on water louse.

Pupa.

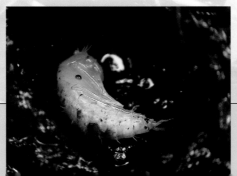

The adult Lesser Silver Water Beetle is quite large, between 14 and 18 mm (about three quarters of an inch) in length. It is a uniform black-brown in colour, though it usually has a slight greenish tinge. The 'feelers' on the head (antennae and palps) are reddish brown in colour, with the antennae having a black club at their tip. The underside of the beetle is densely coated in thick, felty hairs. These repel water, and are used to provide the beetle with an air supply when it is submerged. They give the underside a silvery appearance when the beetle is underwater, and it is this which gives the species its somewhat cumbersome vernacular name.

The best time of year to find the adult beetles is in spring, from March through to May, This being the usual breeding season. In late May and early June the female lays her eggs. These are encased in a silken cocoon that is wrapped in a dead leaf and floats on the surface of the water. The cocoon, though well camouflaged, is very distinctive on account of the silken 'mast' that protrudes from one end of it. The larvae hatch in early- to mid-June. They are equipped with huge jaws and a series of feathery filaments on the abdomen that make them instantly recognisable. They are voracious predators that feed on a variety of invertebrate prey. In their younger stages, they are pale grey-coloured, and swim actively, or rest amongst aquatic vegetation. At this stage, they have been observed feeding on aquatic crustacea, such as copepods and cladocerans. The mature larvae are much darker, and become encrusted with sediment, they are much more sedentary, dwelling amongst the detritus layer, and ambushing water-louse *Asellus* spp.. At this stage, the filaments along the side of the abdomen, which also become encrusted with sediment, provide excellent camouflage for the larvae, breaking up its outline against the background of dead leaves. The larvae grow very rapidly, and in July, after moulting three times, they leave the water and pupate in a cell in the peat. After another two weeks, the adult hatches and returns to the water to over-winter.

In the Somerset Levels, the Lesser Silver Water Beetle favours still, shallow water-bodies with a well-developed organic bottom layer. This thick detritus provides an ideal habitat for the water louse which constitute the main larval prey. A number of the breeding sites discovered during this study dried out completely over the summer, but the very rapid larval development allows *Hydrochara* to complete the aquatic stage of its development before this happens.

Most of the breeding areas in which the Lesser Silver Water Beetle has been found are at least partially shaded by trees, usually willows or birches. This provides the female with a plentiful supply of dead leaves to use during construction of the egg cocoon, and it may also help to prevent an excessive abundance of duckweeds. The egg cocoon is almost invariably positioned in a patch of open water with no duckweed, which presumably affords it better protection from predators. Floating duckweeds *Lemna* spp. (including the alien *L. minuta*) are known to have increased on the Somerset Levels during the last fifty years, with this being a probable consequence of increased eutrophication of the water by agricultural run-off. This in turn may have reduced the range of suitable breeding habitat for the species, especially in permanently wet, less shaded ditches, where the water surface is usually covered with a dense mat of duckweed. Certainly at its Cheshire sites, and elsewhere in Europe, it occurs in permanent, un-shaded water-bodies, and the use of such areas in Somerset may indicate that the species has been forced into sub-optimal habitats by the spread of duckweeds.

Seasonal water bodies also tend to lack vertebrate predators such as fish that might otherwise predate egg cocoons, larvae and adults. Both natural swamp, and artificial ditch habitats are used by the Lesser Silver Water Beetle. The largest breeding colony discovered during the current survey was in an area of seasonally flooded swamp woodland on Shapwick Heath NNR. Good breeding populations have also been found in shallow, partially shaded ditches with thick bottom sediment.

Because of the ephemeral nature of the breeding habitat used by the Lesser Silver Water Beetle, breeding areas move around from one year to another. The adult flies readily, and this enables it to disperse easily to new areas of suitable breeding habitat. Because of this, adults are found in a much wider range of habitats than are the egg cocoons and larvae. They show a strong preference for mats of Floating Sweet-grass *Glyceria fluitans*, in which the adults are very often found, and upon which they probably feed.

The site on Shapwick Heath where *Hydrochara caraboides* was found.

A Rare Water Snail in Somerset – Shining Ram's-horn

Pat Hill-Cottingham

However many ditches one examines, like any other habitat, there is always something new to find – if you are lucky!

I have always been fascinated by freshwater snails, easy to find and catch, and which obligingly crawl around in a dish of water, slowly enough, to allow you to watch their behaviour or even keep for breeding.

It was one late day in September 1997 when a student called me for help with an undergraduate project on the distribution of aquatic organisms in relation to ditch management. She needed advice on possible sites, how to sample, and then how to identify what she found. Little did she, or I, know of the consequences of that chance meeting beside a ditch on one of Somerset Wildlife Trust's (SWT) reserves on the Somerset Levels and Moors. I demonstrated taking the sample and tipped it into a tray, pointing out identification features and showing how to collect the animals into a pot, with Ivy-leaved Duckweed *Lemna trisulca* to provide oxygen and food, so that we could keep them alive whilst identifying them on the kitchen table at home. Later she took other samples from ditches in the area, each under a different management regime.

I thought I would start her on the easy bit; a lot of freshwater invertebrates can be tricky to identify! She tried sorting the molluscs into what she considered

GR

Living *Segmentina nitida* crawling.

GR

PHC

GR

Above: Ditch site.

Above right: *Segmentina* growth stages and millimetre scale.

might be different species and I showed her how to name them. Imagine my immense surprise when I found a rare stranger amongst the familiar species so typical of Somerset's ditches – and not just one, but two specimens. The shell was flat and very shiny – of the type known as ram's-horns, but this was different in that it showed the inner shell thickenings identifying it as the rare (Red Data Book 1) species Shining Ram's-horn *Segmentina nitida*. This species is fairly small, up to about 6mm in diameter and the body of the snail is red due to the presence of the blood pigment, haemoglobin, enabling it to live in low-oxygen conditions – as many of our Somerset ditches are. The shiny shell is beautifully domed on the upper surface and slightly dished on the lower and is so thin that the heart can be seen beating through it. I counted the heart-beat – about 60 times per minute – not much different from our own.

As a new record, I needed verification so I called on Graham Rix, an expert photographer and ecologist to take photographs of the living animal and, having kept the animals alive and well, feeding on Ivy-leaved Duckweed in a dish on the kitchen window sill for two weeks, I took it to London for

A SUB-FOSSIL OF SHINING RAM'S-HORN

Sub-fossils of *Segmentina nitida* were found in 2002 by Kathryn Eales at two sites, Dundon Hayes, Greylake and Briarwood Farm, Greinton and date from 4000-2500BP.

The interesting thing about the sub-fossil is that the shell shares several characteristics with the modern Somerset specimen and these are quite markedly different from another modern shell from the Pevensey Levels in East Sussex, as the pictures show. (How many differences and similarities can you spot?) The east and west populations must have been isolated for many, many years for such evolution to have taken place. I wonder if their DNA matches!

Pat Hill-Cottingham

SOMERSET SUB-FOSSIL	MODERN SPECIMEN FROM SOMERSET	MODERN SPECIMEN FROM EAST SUSSEX

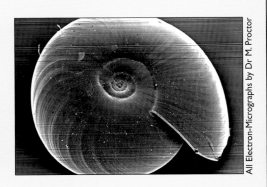
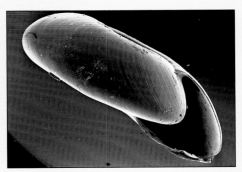

All Electron-Micrographs by Dr M. Proctor

a meeting of the Conchological Society to get the experts there to confirm my identification – so it was Shining Ram's-horn! I rejected all suggestions to send the specimens (dead) to other experts, instead I took the two snails back to the reserve and returned them to their habitat, alive and well.

Questions hit me – how did this species of snail come to live in this particular ditch, which had only been dug in 1986 but which had remained untouched since then? I have found it in no other, on the reserve or elsewhere in Somerset. Until my discovery Shining Ram's-horn had had a distribution limited to eastern England. The last record for Somerset was 1885, taken from an area 'near Long Ashton'. Perhaps it was carried over the Mendips and lay hidden until 1997? I think it is a relict

PHC

Pat, Bill Oddie and cameraman filming on Catcott Moor.

species which has somehow survived the modern methods of ditch cleaning. Credence is lent to this view since sub-fossils have been found recently and we do know that Shining Ram's-horn can tolerate a certain amount of drying-out of its habitat.

In 1998 the discovery hit the local press! Reporters came round to see this rare beastie – and were very surprised to see how tiny it was – I think they had been imagining something far more dramatic! HTV sent a film team around and we sampled the site on a cold February day in 1998, without giving away its exact location. I must admit, I was worried in case we did not find any but my first fishing attempt brought up four beautiful specimens. It received a two minute slot on the HTV news that evening.

The next public appearance was in May 2002 when about four hours of filming brought a similarly short item on the first programme in Bill Oddie's *Going Wild* Series 3 later that year.

Meanwhile, because of the rarity of the species and the fact that it is on the National Priority List of endangered species covered by the Agenda 21, Biodiversity Action Plan for Species and Habitats, I decided that I needed to research its life cycle and ecological requirements – largely unknown when the National Action Plan was written. The whole research programme was built around conservation, so sampling and experiments would not involve killing any of the animals. There was an exception to this, however, when I subjected several species from the ditch to the only predator I could find for Shining Ram's-horn – a small leech called *Glossiphonia heteroclita*.

2001 was a busy year, each month I visited the ditch to take 26 samples at 5 m intervals along its length, to count all the other snail species, and bring home the Shining Ram's-horn to count and measure. So from January 2001 to January 2002 I took and analysed 338 samples – requiring some fortitude in the winter months when on a few occasions I had to break the ice on the surface of the water and when I sank almost to the tops of my Wellingtons in the soggy peat along the banks. In all I measured the diameter of 31 570 snails, collected 234 dead shells and counted 56 731 individuals of other mollusc species!

When I observed captive snails in mini-aquaria at home I discovered that, like many species of snail, Shining Ram's-horn is hermaphrodite but the young are 'born alive', the proper term is ovoviviparous – in other words the eggs are retained in the body of the adult and hatch out as

Lemna trisulca. GR

IVY-LEAVED DUCKWEED *LEMNA TRISULCA* – A SPECIAL SPECIES

Unlike other duckweeds, this species floats below the surface of the still or slow-flowing water of Wetland ditches. This has the advantage, to animals, of releasing all its oxygen into the body of the water, where it is used in respiration. There are no true stems or leaves, instead the plant consists of a series of branching fronds with tiny roots hanging down into the water. The fronds are about 7-12 mm long, narrow and lanceolate, growing at right angles to each other. The thin, soft, texture of these fronds makes this plant the main food for herbivores. Indeed, it could be said to be an indicator of a diverse assemblage of aquatic animals.

Pat Hill-Cottingham

GR

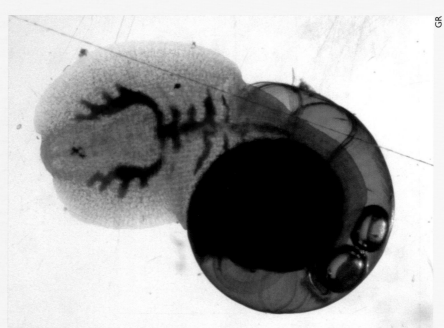

GR

Above: Leech *Glossiphonia heteroclita* entering shell.

Above right: Leech digesting *S. nitida*.

GR

Lemna trisulca grazed by *S. nitida*.

baby snails. This means that they are protected throughout their embryonic life and the numbers of young produced are fewer – in this species I recorded a mean of 9.4 young per adult. This birth rate enabled the overall population to show an increase of 46 individuals per sample over a year. Whether this increase could be maintained without extending the habitat is, so far, an unanswered question!

One day, whilst measuring a sample of snails I found the head of a leech, *Glossiphonia heteroclita* extended deep into the body whorl of a snail. My immediate reaction was to remove the leech and save the snail, instead I watched, fascinated, to see what would happen. The snail was young, just 2 mm across and the leech 2.5 mm long, 6 mm when extended. The head end of the leech was well inside the body whorl and it had everted its pharynx. Juices secreted by the leech dissolve the tissues of the snail so that they can be 'hoovered' up into the gut of the leech. The leech has no anus so the food it takes in is predigested with no solid waste. Gradually, branches of the leech gut were filled; every so often the pharynx would withdraw a little and missed particles sucked up. As different parts of the snail were reached, the colour of the food entering the leech changed, first the dark pigmented head and mantle, then the red of the heart and finally the darker red-brown of the hepato-pancreas, deep in the inner coils of the shell. After 30 minutes the shell was empty, not a trace of the body to hide its beauty, and the leech withdrew to sleep off its meal.

Having drawn these events, photographer Graham Rix and I, having collected more snails and a leech, photographed the whole feeding procedure. What was interesting was that it took about 20 minutes to persuade the leech to attack, in spite of its empty gut (one can see the gut through the body wall and thus assess whether it has fed recently). It appeared that a meeting with a snail was pure chance, there seemed to be no chemical attraction and the snail made no attempt to escape – it simply retracted its body deep into the body whorl and blew a couple of bubbles which only served to hamper the photography! Another experiment showed that the leech was not at all fussy as to which species it ate, it sampled all five species it was offered! In spite of all this evidence of predation, it is unlikely that the leech could seriously deplete snail populations. Only eight of this species of leech were found throughout the year and no other leech species found in the ditch appeared to attack the molluscs.

A far more important factor required for the occurrence of Shining Ram's-horn in a ditch is the presence of vegetation. This species needs a highly vegetated, undisturbed ditch, with lots of emergent plants (it can climb out of the water and crawl a few centimetres up the stems) – just the sort of late-succession ditch, for example, that farmers need to clean out in order to keep an efficient 'wet fence' for containing livestock! This is where conservation can come into conflict with farming. However, the reserve containing Shining Ram's-horn is also farmed, traditionally, with late hay harvesting and after-grazing by cattle, so it is possible to have both open ditches maintained as wet fences and other non-drainage ditches that can be left to vegetate fully. Another rare snail in Somerset, Round-mouthed Valve Snail *Valvata macrostoma*, is also found in well-vegetated ditches so we do have a need, within the County, for bodies of water that can be left to reach a late-succession stage.

So what is happening now with Somerset's only population of Shining Ram's-horn? SWT has been given a new management plan for the species, derived from the research, and steps are in hand to extend the ditch system to provide other undisturbed plant-filled ditches into which it can spread. We do have one big problem and that is the time factor. It takes between 6-10 years for a ditch to become a suitable habitat so we shall probably be planting some emergents in the new ditch to speed up the process, meanwhile the snail is highly vulnerable, especially with recent dry summers when the water in the ditch has dropped to a few centimetres.

Somerset's ditches are rich in invertebrate life. The more we can learn about invertebrate life cycles and understand their habitat requirements, the more possible it will be to conserve these fascinating animals. It remains to be seen whether global warming and increasing extremes of weather will make our efforts in conservation a waste of time!

Dragonflies on the Levels

Philip Radford

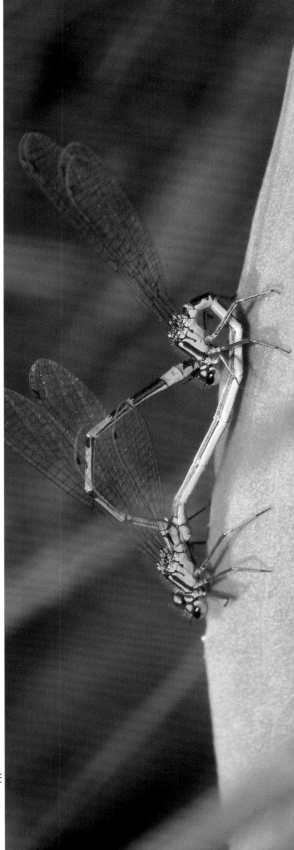

Considering the large numbers of peaty pools and rhynes, as drainage channels across the Somerset Levels, together with some slow-flowing rivers, it is not surprising that the area supports a good, variable dragonfly population. Further, there are some well-managed marsh reserves which doubtless increase the number of dragonfly species with their specialised ways of life. The Somerset Levels are ideal for observing all aspects of dragonfly behaviour.

Dragonflies spend much of their lives underwater where they eat small aquatic insects; they are meat-eaters in the water and also when they emerge to become airborne, so a good supply of mosquitoes and midges is necessary. At least for me, no insect group is more fascinating than that of the drag-onflies, with the flying insect showing bright, Iridescent and reflective colours with distinct and constant patterns. Moreover, using their two pairs of wings, dragonflies can hover or fly forwards, backwards or sideways with ease, best seen when aerial prey is being hunted or male is chasing female. In addition, dragonflies mate in a unique fashion in a ring or wheel position, with the female receiving the male's sperm from the underside of the front of his abdomen. This may sound surpris-ing; perhaps even more so is the fact that another male dragonfly can displace the sperm of the previous partner!

Dragonflies include the small, graceful and weak-flying damselflies with wings of nearly the same shape, and the more powerful, large dragonflies with differently shaped wings. Both groups are well represented on the Levels, although the larger dragonflies are scarce where there is little shelter from strong winds. So, if you want to look at big dragonflies, it is best to pick a calm, warm day to watch them, and. there should be plenty of damselflies about also. The large dragonflies, having emerged from their larval cases, may fly considerable distances to find suitable food insects; in contrast, damselflies feed low down and close to the water from where they emerged. After emergence, drag-onflies take a week or two to acquire their full colouring,

The first hawker dragonfly to be on the wing in May is the Hairy Dragonfly *Brachytron pratense*. Male Hairies are patterned in blue; they have large eyes like all dragonflies, and which are very conspicuous as territories are patrolled. The thorax is downy, thus retaining heat and so helping the dragonfly to survive during a night frost. Hairy Dragonflies are scarce generally in Britain; they have a short flight season and happily, the Levels have a reasonable population.

Another notable Levels draqonfly is the Southern Hawker *Aeshna cyanea*, normally first seen in flight during late June. When mature, the male's abdomen is patterned segmentally with green spots on a dark background, while the end portion is in bright blue. After mating, the females often lay their eggs in damp peat near a pond or lake; commonly, the females are quite preoccupied and permit a really close approach, which is helpful for photographers. Southern Hawkers on their territories are inquisitive insects and may surprise the observer by their close approach.

The largest Levels dragonfly, and probably that with the most agile flight is the Emperor *Anax imperator*; the male can be readily identified by the black line down the back of its blue abdomen, The male Emperor seems quite tireless when watched as it patrols its territory; intruders are quickly chased off and even falling leaves are sometimes intercepted. Of course, as with all the dragonfly group, dark clouds or the onset of rain will mean a retreat into cover. It is a thrilling experience, on a warm June or July day, to watch an Emperor chasing after large prey items, such as butterflies.

Emerging in late May, the brown Four-spotted Chaser *Libellula quadrimaculata* is very common over the Levels. I find it a remarkable species as mating occurs in flight and lasts only a few seconds, although many other species, when mating, remain connected for hours on end, and often at rest on vegetation. Four-spotted Chasers are the favourite prey of Hobbies; the falcon will tear off the insect's wings in the air and transfer the abdomen to the beak with a talon. Not infrequently, individual Blackbirds or wagtails will habitually seize emerging and helpless dragonflies soon after dawn; there is a heavy mortality, as in much of nature. It is commonplace for damselflies to become trapped on spiders' webs, snapped up by swooping Swallows or even be digested by sundew plants.

Another chaser found in the area is the handsome, Broad-bodied *L. depressa*; here the mature male has a blue abdomen while that of the female is a yellow-brown. The males can be very aggressive to other chasers and also towards unresponsive females; torn wings, as evidence of conflict, are commonplace. Yet another beautiful insect, when mature, is the Black-tailed Skimmer *Orthetrum*

Four-spotted Chaser *Libellula quadrimaculata* male.

Opposite page: Southern Hawker *Aeshna cyanea* male. PR

145

ALL PHOTOGRAPHS PR

Common Darter *Sympetrum striolatum* mating.

Large Red Damselfly *Pyrrosoma nymphula* mating.

Azure Damselfly *Coenagrion puella* mating.

Migrant Hawker *Aeshna mixta* mating.

Southern Hawker *Aeshna cyanea* male and exuvium.

cancellatum. The males commonly fly at Westhay during July, often settling for rest on the ground; the abdomen is a pruinose blue, with yellow spotting at the side and a black end. Skimmers are very vigilant and, in consequence are difficult to photograph when sunning.

In late summer, darter dragonflies predominate on the Levels, with the Common Sympetrum *Sympetrum striolatum* occurring in large numbers. The male is red and the female straw-coloured; mating pairs in ring are sometimes easy to approach at rest on a plant and can make attractive photographs. The Ruddy Darter *S. sanguineum* is smaller; males are bright red and have black legs. This species was once nationally endangered but, happily, numbers are now good in Somerset. Then Migrant Hawkers *A. mixta* were once scarce too but are now plentiful in late summer; they are small hawkers and delightfully patterned.

Turning now to, the slim and graceful damselflies, the largest is the Banded Demoiselle *Calopteryx splendens*, emerging near slow-flowing rivers and, also, the same type of habitat supports the well-named White-legged Damselfly *Platycnemis pennipes*. The earliest damselfly to emerge on the Levels is the large red *Pyrrosoma nymphula*; it looks particularly attractive at rest on fresh spring foliage. The commonest damselfly in the area is the Azure *Coenagrion puella*, with characteristic black designs on the blue abdomen. Female Azures lay eggs into submerged plants with males in tandem above. Often several females oviposit together, submerged in air bubbles, while the males appear to be standing on the water surface! The smallest damsel is the Blue-tailed *Ischnura elegans*; it is abundant and, interestingly, females show different colour forms. Other blue damsels present include the Common Blue *Enallagma cyathigerum* (often abundant) and the Variable *C. pulchellum*, which is nationally scarce.

Finally, the Levels can boast Red-eyed Damsels *Erythromma najas*; these distinctive insects rest especially on water-lily or pondweed leaves, a beautiful sight on a sunny June day. Certainly no summer day is better spent, or is more rewarding; than when searching for dragonflies over the Somerset Levels.

Male Banded Demoiselle
Calopteryx splendeus.

Butterflies

Keith Gould

My first recollections of the levels were from the windows of a train on a journey to Paddington with my parents and brother to stay with an auntie and uncle for Christmas nearly fifty years ago. As we travelled towards Langport I was amazed to see this lakeland with a few sad houses and rows of odd shaped trees sticking up out of all the water, flooding that year was apparently very bad. My father explained a little about the Levels but it did not mean much.

I first really renewed my acquaintance with the Levels at the age of twelve when a group from my school used to travel out to Shapwick with Dr. Ernest Neal in his old Austin Traveller. This weekly outing in the summer months was entitled rather grandly "Biological Fieldwork" and we did indeed study many things. At this time the Somerset and Dorset Railway was still running and Shapwick station with its tiny station complete with signal box and level crossing added another distraction accompanied as it was by the occasional steam train. The area was at the time quite a busy place with the Eclipse Peat Company whose tiny miniature railway chugged across the Levels dragging the tiny conical trucks along the South Drain.

The place on a sunny day had a heavy humid air to it, quite different from the town, and at times the shade of the many Willow, Alder and Birch trees was welcomed. These were examined carefully for caterpillars with many exciting finds resulting. The discovery of your first Puss Moth larva chomping away with its bright green colour and handsome brownish saddle, and, to cap it all, the whip like prongs on the tail, is never forgotten. The Poplar Hawk moth also produced splendid eating machines and in due course the well marked adults could be found, one drowned in a ditch. This specimen I was allowed to keep but collecting of other specimens was strictly forbidden.

These rides also provided splendid habitats for butterflies. The earliest I can recall was the Orange Tip. We searched until cross eyed for the tiny orange conical eggs laid on the tips of the Garlic Mustard plants and under a hand lens the incredible detail of the ribbed egg could be seen. On

KG

Above: Egg of Orange Tip.

Top right: Marsh Fritillary, Buckland Wood.

Below right: Large Red Damselfly, West Sedgemoor.

subsequent visits more searching revealed the larvae, usually only one to a plant, standing up like a seed pod from the stalk. The males with their bright orange tips were easily seen whereas the females lurked in the undergrowth using the amazing moss green camouflage to protect them.

A less common occurrence was the occasional sighting of a Clouded Yellow. These powered up and down the drains in full sunshine taking the odd sip from Hemp Agrimony flowers. These were indeed frustrating as they were very wary and did not open their wings, giving little chance to observe them properly. Dr Neal caught one for us and explained that they had probably come all the way from France, an amazing journey for something so small.

The star butterfly without doubt was the Marsh Fritillary situated, from memory, fairly near the station. I had a copy of Edmund Sanders book "A Butterfly Book for the Pocket" as a birthday present and had spent hours poring over the pictures and memorising the details. I was not to be disappointed, we found the larval webs with the caterpillars sunning themselves on top and, later on in late May, the adults. These were so beautiful with the bright orange colours glinting in the sun and a mating pair showed the details of the underside to perfection. My attempts to take pictures with a plastic bodied black and white film camera proved a disaster.

During our many visits we pond-dipped, watched birds, spied on dragonflies, studied orchids and collected various grasses, sedges and reeds. Many unusual sights and observations were made and the area became quite familiar, only brought to an end by the onset of A Levels and leaving school.

It was to be many years later when I began to revisit the Levels and some of the old places. This time I had a wife in tow who was fortunately very interested in wildlife and butterflies. I had joined Butterfly Conservation and was carrying out conservation work as a volunteer on various sites and giving talks to interested parties on our work.

By this time the railway was long gone and in its place was a useful track beside the South drain that gave excellent access to the countryside. Peat digging, it would seem, had almost ceased and many of the old diggings had become nature reserves. One of our favourite walks is from Ashcott Comer towards Shapwick along the drain to the bridge crossing the drain. On the way there are many butterfly food plants in good amounts due to the rich spoil dredged from the drain. Nettles abound in places and during most years the massed tents of the Small Tortoiseshell larva may be found

Southern Marsh Orchid, Catcott.

Gatekeeper.

Brimstone, Shapwick.

Lesser Butterfly Orchid.

although later in the season their numbers will be cut back by predation from parasitic wasps. The Orange Tips and Green Veined Whites flutter around the Cuckoo Flowers and I have seen the occasional Clouded Yellow hurtling along trying to catch a train. Another migrant that seems to be doing well with the current warming of our climate is the Painted Lady, it is thought that the milder drier winters are allowing larger numbers to over-winter here and reinforced by migrants from the Continent are becoming commoner.

The Comma butterfly is another success story, once a pest in Hop fields in Kent it has changed its food plant to Elm and finally Nettles and moved steadily north. On the Levels I have seen good numbers of these, indeed on bird watching trips to Ashcott in late September many were noted prior to their hibernation.

On reaching the bridge a choice must be made, left down the drove or right over the bridge. In July I would suggest that you go right and proceed through the wood towards the bird hide. Near the

KG

White Admiral, Shapwick.

hide, if you are lucky and the day is sunny, a wonderful sight may reward you. This is one of the few places in Somerset that you can still see the White Admiral in flight. They spend most of their time flitting around the tops of the trees only coming down to drink nectar from the Bramble flowers. I think it is the British butterfly with the most beautiful underside of all with the delicate pastel shades of blue, fawn and tan. The larval food-plant is Honeysuckle, the favoured plants being those that send single stems up into the canopy and although I have searched I have never found eggs, larva or pupa, they seem so well concealed. This small area supports a fairly stable population and records show there may be signs of this lovely insect spreading.

Flitting from patch to patch of sunshine, the Speckled Wood is an early butterfly seen here, reminding us of the season to come, the males defending their tiny territories against all comers. Later on the Red Admiral makes a welcome appearance adding to the charm of this small wood.

If we took the left hand turn from the drove and walked towards the new built hide on stilts we pass an area that was, last July, full of Brimstone butterflies. Both male and females were identified energetically soaring up and around the glade stopping only for the occasional sip of nectar from the many flowers. They have the best of both worlds, a good summer then a long sleep before the final burst to procreate the following year. The males, with their bright sulphur-yellow wings and their pale yellow, almost white partners, put on quite a show. The females can be confused with Large Whites, but look for the black tips on the wings that give away the Large White. Many other butterflies can be found: Skippers, Tortoiseshells and various Browns.

I could continue with the wonders of the Levels with moth trapping, dragonflies, beautiful plants such as the Royal Fern and the multitude of bird life present. All I would conclude with is that this unique area with its traditional work methods and farming are under constant threat from developments of one sort or another. We should be grateful for the work of the many conservation bodies that carry out so much work often with little thanks and often much criticism. I hope their work continues and that the Levels remain to act as inspiration for future generations after I am long gone.

KG

Marsh Fritillary

Birds in a Changing Landscape

Sally Mills

As a landscape area, the Somerset Levels and Moors has changed dramatically over the last 10,000 years. Initially changes were predominantly caused by climate and natural events, but in recent times, human effect on the area has been dramatic. During these periods of transition, bird life has altered in response to the habitats and conditions created. The recent impact of human habitation on the moor has caused major habitat loss, resulting in a predictable knock-on effect to bird species. However, at the same time, this impact has opened up new opportunities for some of our declining wildlife, particularly those reliant and associated with wetland habitats. With developments that have occurred in recent times as an indication of what can be achieved, the immediate future looks quite promising for our wetland wildlife.

This account focuses on the area of the Levels and Moors now known as the Avalon Marshes, which is made up of the northern and southern peat production zones within the Brue Valley. My aim is to touch on the broad changes that have led to the landscape we see today, focusing on the new opportunities to address national habitat and species decline, and suggest what this could mean for the future.

The last 10,000 years have seen some major broad habitat changes, beginning at the time when the sea covered the Avalon Marshes. When we look at the landscape of today, it is hard to picture a scene of rocky shores and shallow salt water that used to dominate this valley. The bird life of that time would have been similar to what we might see today on some of our southern continental coasts, such as now the very rare Dalmatian Pelican.

Over the next few thousand years changing climate and sea levels altered the landscape dramatically. There was the development of freshwater habitats, bringing with them birds such as terns, herons

Heron. RW

and waders. The range of habitats that established would have included fen, reed-bed, wet scrub and carr woodland. As a result, the slow process of peat formation began, together with the colonisation of specialist flora and fauna tolerant of the acid conditions being created, such as sphagnum, sundew and cotton grass. Typical birds of this time would have been waders such as Curlew and Snipe.

Approximately 6000 years ago and up to as recently as a few thousand years ago, the moors remained very wet throughout the year. During the winter months especially, they were a very inhospitable place to be, life was difficult and humans had to work hard to survive. However, this kind of exis-tence and the problems faced, meant that both man and the moor could exist side by side. The poor wet winter conditions of this flooded landscape limited access on to the moor and so the impact of humans was restricted to the drier months. However, approximately 400 years ago, this changed; people started to cope with the conditions and applied their intelligence to turning that once hostile place into one that could be exploited.

Human impact was dramatic. Drainage, and later peat extraction, had a major effect on birdlife. Effective drainage of large areas meant freshwater habitats were lost and peat bogs dried out. Mechanisation in recent years has exacerbated this impact. Large machines have meant that the land-scape could be ripped apart driven by a continual demand for peat, fuelled predominately by the horticultural business.

This series of events brings us to the present day in the Avalon Marshes. What we see now is a linear landscape created by peat extraction. After the peat has been removed down to the level of the clay beneath, and with the cessation of artificial drainage, the large holes remaining fill with water, to the levels held in the surrounding ditches. All land with current planning permission for extraction has to undergo restoration once extraction ceases. Ownership of these areas is now shared between nature conservation bodies (the Royal Society for the Protection of Birds (RSPB), Somerset Wildlife Trust and English Nature), and many private individuals.

The RSPB saw this as an opportunity to help address the decline of some of our wetland habitats, predominantly reed-bed. Although the preferred scenario would be to prevent peat extraction from being undertaken, these new holes in the ground, destined to fill up with water, were quite a unique opportunity for wetland restoration. Reed-bed is one of the habitats that has suffered most from drainage, lack of management and human impact. It was once an extensive habitat, partic-

Top: Ham Wall RSPB Reserve: reed-bed is one of the habitats that has suffered most from drainage, lack of management and human impact.

Above: The conversion of the worked-out peat areas in the Avalon Marshes which has reverted to declining wetland habitats involves major, expensive engineering work, such as the installation of banks, ditches and sluices.

Right: Bittern.

ularly in eastern England, until the major drainage schemes of the 17th century. Intensification of drainage between 1945 and 1970 led to further deterioration and between 1979 and 1993 there was a net loss of reed-bed in England of 5-10%, resulting from grazing, built development and waste tipping. A survey in 1994 revealed 926 reed-bed sites in UK amounting to 6530ha; however, a large percentage of this area was fragmented into small blocks of less than a hectare in size. Just 15 sites exceeded 40 ha, only 1140 ha of the total area. The tidal reed-bed at the Tay estuary at 410 ha is the largest area of contiguous reed in the country; saline incursion limits its ability to support a wide range of reed-bed flora and fauna. The effect of this loss of reed-bed habitat has meant that specialised birds such as the Bittern have declined massively, down to just 11 booming males in 1997.

The conversion of the worked out peat areas in the Avalon Marshes back to wetland habitat involves major, expensive engineering work. The main objective in the outset is hydrological control. Structures need to be installed to enable water to be controlled both for the establishment and the future management of wetland habitats. Once pumping for peat extraction ceases, structures such as banks and sluices need to be in place to control rising water levels. The linear excavations often left by peat extraction may mean that ground re-profiling will need to be undertaken. Desired ground elevation levels for the optimum water depth for our target wetland habitats and their wildlife can then be created. Ditch and water feature excavation is an essential part of wetland restoration, to provide important water edge, and channels for the establishment and movement of invertebrate and fish populations.

The RSPB targets three main bird species as of conservation concern for the Avalon Marshes, classified as 'red' and 'amber', depending on rarity and vulnerability.

There are approximately 50 booming, red listed, Bittern males in the country, (the population being assessed through the call of the male, which is a boom noise similar to that producing by blowing over the top of a bottle). The main reason for its decline has been habitat loss, predominantly by drainage and lack of management of suitable habitat. It needs wet reed-beds, which provide a readily available food supply and essential cover for breeding and wintering. The movement of fish through the wetland is vital, wet features and profiles that make fish more available are important features in a newly created wetland for Bitterns.

Opposite page:
Nesting swan, Westhay.   LN

Long-tailed Tits flit from tree to tree along the droves.

Heron.

The amber listed Marsh Harrier has also suffered from habitat loss and persecution by humans, a significant threat being the effects of pesticides such that, in 1971, the population was reduced to only one pair in the country. Marsh Harriers like large areas of reed, up to 100ha, which provide cover and opportunities for feeding on young birds, their typical prey.

The Bearded Tit is also amber listed. Quite stable in its numbers, it is still vulnerable to habitat changes and to cold winter weather. It is a species requiring a good source of insects in the summer to feed the young and then in the winter to feeding on seeds. Bearded Tits are often found using the drier areas of reed for nesting and the wetter areas for summer feeding.

There are other target species for determining habitat creation in the Avalon Marshes. One is the Barn Owl. The Somerset Levels and Moors is a strong-hold for the Barn Owl and the population is doing well. Special attention must be given to providing habitat for this 'dry' species in what is a very wetland landscape. Barn Owls are particularly vulnerable again to pesticides, road traffic, loss of habitat and inclement weather during the breeding season. They rely on a good structured grass sward, which will support high populations of the small mammals which form their major prey.

The Reed Warbler is, as its name suggests, a species that relies on reed-bed habitat. Populations have exploded in the Avalon Marshes. At Ham Wall alone, since 1995, the population has gone from 2 to 370. Shoveler is an example of one of the duck species that has colonised the area – as a surface feeder it requires shallow, permanent, vegetation-fringed pools. Other species such as Gadwall, for which the Avalon Marshes is now nationally important, again likes shallow open water with plenty of cover and fringing vegetation, it also requires dry banks and islands. Garganey, one of our rarer ducks needs plenty of cover, sheltered shallow water with floating emergent vegetation. The Little Grebe is another success, needing deeper water to catch insects, amphibian larvae and small fish – together with the better known Great Crested Grebe, which likes deeper water and feeds more on fish. Both are excellent indicators of a wetland system that is starting to mature, with good food supplies.

In addition, there are the opportunistic birds that use the range of transitional habitats created during the process of wetland restoration. Birds such as Redshank and Lapwing are always very quick to take advantage of such areas. They both look for ground with sparse vegetation so potential predators may be seen, and shallow splashy areas with a, good supply of insects for feeding young. Redshank like a little cover and soft ground to find worms and larvae, Lapwings require open views and feed more on invertebrates.

There is no doubt that the restoration of the Avalon Marshes to a landscape scale wetland is providing essential habitat for many of our declining wetland species. Over 700ha has now been restored for nature conservation with many more opportunities arising in the future.

Reed Warbler at home amongst the reeds.

SUMMARY OF NATIONALLY IMPORTANT BREEDING SPECIES IN THE AVALON MARSHES		
Species	Number	Summary of increase between 1996 & 2002
Cetti's Warbler	146 males	Over 100%
Gadwall	144 pairs	Over 100%
Garganey	7 pairs	Up to 50%
Little Grebe	161 pairs	Over 50%
Pochard	19 pairs	Over 100%
Reed Warbler	1159 singing males	Over 100%
Shoveler	20 pairs	Over 50%
Water Rail	119 calling males	Over 100%

The development of the Avalon marshes for nature conservation, brings with it added community benefit, increased education opportunities and more prospects for leisure, as at the RSPB's Ham Wall Reserve.

Disabled access at Ham Wall Reserve.

Local people seize opportunities to get closer to their local environment, by undertaking volunteering work.

162

Another significant aspect of this changing landscape is the village communities which lie within it. The area is an important resource for local people who now become increasingly involved as the Avalon Marshes concept evolves. The area is an excellent educational resource for local schools and colleges, volunteers seize opportunities to get closer to their local environment, and specialists use the area to record habitat change and their effect on species populations. The Levels and Moors Partnership is working within these communities to promote local services, products and village facilities. Tourism in the Avalon Marshes may well have a significant part to play, as this major inland wetland continues to evolve.

The future of this landscape is a very exciting one, although the effects of issues such as climate change, are still very uncertain. However, the immediate future as peat extraction continues, will again mean habitat loss, but could continue to present more opportunities for wetland birds and associated wildlife. As the size of wetland area expands and matures, its importance for nature conservation will continue to increase. This will bring with it added community benefit, increased education opportunities and more prospects for leisure. There is no doubt that this area we have come to know as the Avalon Marshes has the capability to develop into the most important inland wetland in the country.

Winter Waterfowl on the Somerset Levels and Moors at Night

David Chown

The Somerset Levels and Moors are renowned for supporting internationally important wintering populations of several wildfowl and wader species, notably Bewick's Swan, Wigeon, Gadwall, Teal, Pintail, Shoveler, Golden Plover and Lapwing. However, in typical conditions the casual visitor may wonder where all the birds are. This is because, except during the usually brief periods of extensive flooding, by day these birds (especially the duck) tend to be concentrated on a few refuge areas, particularly West Sedgemoor RSPB reserve (which can hold in excess of 20000 Wigeon and Teal), but also the Somerset Wildlife Trust's Catcott Lows reserve, Shapwick Heath NNR, and recently, one or two of the Raised Water Level Areas (RWLAs; see below). Here there are sufficiently large pools of open water, free from shooting disturbance, to provide birds with refuge. The importance of open water for security can be seen in the response of a flock of grazing Wigeon to the appearance of a hunting Peregrine – a head-long rush, en masse, to the refuge of an adjacent pool, a sight with which some birders will be familiar.

Dusk dispersal of wildfowl from refuge areas on the Levels has long been known to occur, and before there were protected reserves, wildfowl which had spent the daylight hours at Bridgwater Bay NNR would flight into the Levels after sunset, as old-timers in the shooting fraternity will testify. Furthermore, we know from research elsewhere that nocturnal feeding occurs in many waterfowl species.

In December 2000/01, I started a three-winter survey for English Nature which aimed to discover more about the extent of nocturnal feeding in key waterfowl species on the Levels. Did the dispersal involve many of the birds present in refuge areas by day? Where did they go, and what habitats did they use?

Cormorants, Shapwick. LN

Our limited understanding of what happens on the Levels at night was due largely to the practical difficulty of observing birds at night. For the purposes of the survey I was lent a night-sight by the Environment Agency. This offered reasonable visibility assuming that some moonlight was available. Under cloud cover, or around the new moon, conditions were more difficult, so most survey work was conducted under moonlight. For obvious reasons, I was invariably accompanied by a second observer (Jon Stirling or Rich Taylor) during nocturnal survey, and duly managed to avoid walking into any ditches!

Fieldwork was always conducted in the first part of the night – from about two hours after sunset until midnight. All survey areas were on sites south of the Polden ridge. In winter 2000/01, study areas on some 33 widespread sites (including three which were flooded at the time) were visited once each. In the next two winters, study areas on six moors, King's Sedgemoor, North Moor, Southlake Moor, West Sedgemoor, West Moor and Wet Moor, were each surveyed two to four times per winter. No surveying was done when sites were flooded.

Each site was also visited on the day of, or following, the nocturnal visits, to record day-time water-fowl numbers and habitat features including the extent and depth of standing water, and vegetation characteristics. Simple statistical analyses were performed to investigate relationships between species' distribution and habitat.

The results of the study, summarized for the three most numerous species in Tables 1 to 3 below, were something of a revelation: it's one thing to observe waterfowl departing from refuge areas at dusk, quite another to see these birds, sometimes in substantial numbers, scattered across sites where there had been none during the day. Wigeon, Teal and Lapwing were present on the vast majority of nocturnal site-visits, and Pintail and Shoveler on a moderate number. Unlike the wildfowl, Lapwing were often present in day-time too, sometimes in larger numbers, but they were much more dispersed at night. Bewick's Swan, Gadwall and Golden Plover were rarely recorded. Snipe and Dunlin were more widespread on some sites than they were in day-time, but these species were not recorded systematically.

Note that the summarized results in Tables 1 to 3 are intended to give an idea of the scale of nocturnal presence, not a rigorous comparison between winters (the survey areas and schedule in 2000/01 were very different from those in the following winters).

Lapwing flock. RW

Top: Widgeon.

Above: Teal.

Top right: Lapwing.

Right: Teal.

Table 1. Night-time and day-time counts and densities of the most commonly recorded key waterfowl species in nocturnal survey areas in winter 2000/01. The counts are from 30 sites (three sites surveyed while flooded are excluded) with a total area of 1354ha, visited once each.

		Total count	No of sites on which species was recorded (out of 30)	Average density (birds/ha)
Wigeon	Night	2283	25	1.69
	Day	50	1	0.04
Teal	Night	1897	26	1.40
	Day	2	2	0.001
Lapwing	Night	1202	28	0.89
	Day	3615	16	2.67

Table 2. Night-time and day-time counts and densities of the most commonly recorded key waterfowl species in nocturnal survey areas in winter 2001/02. The counts are from six sites with a total area of 341ha, visited two to four times each (cumulative area surveyed: 1028ha).

		Total count	No of sites on which species was recorded (out of 30)	Average density (birds/ha)
Wigeon	Night	3879	16	3.77
	Day	0	0	0
Teal	Night	565	16	0.55
	Day	130	1	0.13
Lapwing	Night	745	15	0.72
	Day	524	5	0.51

Table 3. Night-time and day-time counts and densities of the most commonly recorded key waterfowl species in nocturnal survey areas in winter 2002/03. The counts are from five sites with a total area of 315ha, visited three times each (cumulative area surveyed: 945ha).

		Total count	No of sites on which species was recorded (out of 30)	Average density (birds/ha)
Wigeon	Night	1567	14	1.66
	Day	0	0	0
Teal	Night	445	14	0.47
	Day	0	0	0
Lapwing	Night	149	12	0.16
	Day	1312	4	1.39

Lapwing.

It is inevitable that many birds will have been overlooked during nocturnal surveys, so the figures above will be under-estimates. Teal, especially, were easily missed, being particularly scattered (see Table 4), often obscured in vegetation, and remaining silent when flushed. It is likely that Teal numbers were at least double those located. On the other hand, Wigeon, which usually occurred in small flocks, were more visible on the ground. Dispersed feeding Lapwing could also be inconspicuous in less than ideal conditions, and roosting flocks preferred fields with rushes or other cover and were therefore easily missed.

The remaining key waterfowl species were recorded in much smaller numbers. Bewick's Swans were recorded only twice at night (36 birds) and once by day in the nocturnal survey areas. The species is well-known for roosting communally on open water, so the lack of dispersal at night was expected.

Excluding flooded sites, just four Gadwall were recorded at night and two by day. This species' habits are very different from the other dabbling duck, being associated more with permanent waters, chiefly the Avalon Marshes. Even when flooded, grassland sites only attract moderate numbers of Gadwall.

Forty-six Pintail were recorded at night on nine site-visits in winter 2000/01, when particularly large numbers of Pintail were present on the Levels, but over the next two winters only six birds were found on three site-visits. No Pintail were seen by day in any nocturnal survey area.

Shoveler were encountered rather more frequently than Pintail, a total of 101 birds at night on 18 site-visits, but again, none were present by day. Like the previous species, Shoveler were probably under-recorded to some extent among the larger numbers of Wigeon and Teal – even with a night-sight, identification of duck at night can be tricky!

Surprisingly, just two Golden Plover were found at night, and a total of 212 by day on four site-visits. I have seen large flocks departing from diurnal roosts around sunset, and suspect that nocturnal dispersal may be substantial. If this is so, it seems that they travel to feeding sites beyond the flood-plain, perhaps to arable farmland. In a recent study in arable areas in eastern England, Golden Plover were found to rely heavily on nocturnal feeding.

Study areas on West Sedgemoor, closest to the main refuge, had the highest densities of Wigeon and Teal in 2000/01, but there was little to suggest that waterfowl departing from West Sedgemoor concentrated on the nearest sites. Given the flight capabilities of these species, the distances between refuge and

Mute swans.

feeding areas on the Levels are unlikely to be a barrier. Birds recorded on some of the more northerly survey areas (e.g. Walton Moor and the north side of King's Sedgemoor) could have come from day-time refuges north of the Poldens, such as Catcott Lows and Shapwick Heath NNR.

A fascinating aspect of the results was the very scattered night-time distribution. We think of Wigeon, Teal and Lapwing as very gregarious birds by day. At night, the numbers in any one field were usually small (see median counts per occupied field in Table 4), while the proportion of fields which held birds on any given night was substantial, though variable. Cumulatively, over the multiple visits of winters 2001/02 and 2002/03, Wigeon were recorded in 46% of fields in the survey areas, Teal in 55% and Lapwing in 64%. Over the three winters, counts of duck (all key species combined) were under 50 in 89% of occupied fields.

Table 4. The percentage of fields in survey areas which held key waterfowl species on a given night, and the median count of those species per occupied field.

		2000/01	2001/02	2002/03
Wigeon	% of fields in which the species was recorded	21	13	24
	Median count per occupied field	7	18	11
Teal	% of fields in which the species was recorded	28	15	26
	Median count per occupied field	3	4	3
Lapwing	% of fields in which the species was recorded	33	27	13
	Median count per occupied field	2	3	1

Wigeon droppings, recorded during habitat monitoring, provided evidence of the presence of Wigeon in fields where none were found at the time of survey. Including these fields, at least 40% of fields in the widespread 2000/01 survey areas were used by Wigeon, and at least 61% of fields over the multiple visits in 2001/02 and 2002/03.

Most duck dispersal occurred before fieldwork started. Movements of duck overhead were more frequent in the limited amount of survey conducted within 21/2 hours of sunset than subsequently. This agrees with observations of duck departing from the West Sedgemoor refuge, which occurred between 30 minutes and two hours after sunset. There was no suggestion of a resumption of movements in the latter stages of nocturnal visits, and therefore no evidence that duck start to return to refuges before midnight.

Canada Goose.

Lapwings disperse a little earlier than duck. Visit the Levels around dusk – just as it becomes too dark to see – and you will hear the calls of Lapwings passing low overhead, seemingly on a broad front, heading for feeding areas. This is also borne out by observations of departures from the West Sedgemoor refuge, where dispersal occurred between 30 and 90 minutes after sunset.

The analysis of night-time waterfowl distribution in relation to habitat features highlighted the importance of standing water for duck in all three winters. However, it is the shallowest water, under 10cm in depth, that is most beneficial for Wigeon and Teal feeding at night. These conditions are rarely used by day (unless deeper water is also available), for reasons which were described earlier. Dry fields were almost entirely avoided. This finding is in keeping with the suggestion that Wigeon have a physiological need to drink frequently while feeding, and in the case of Teal, may reflect the fact that the presence of water or mud facilitates their dabbling feeding action. High counts of Pintail and Shoveler on the Levels are very strongly associated with periods of flooding, reflecting these species' preference for rather deeper water. Some Pintail used shallow 'splash' conditions at night. Shoveler seem to be more-or-less restricted to water deep enough to enable feeding by swimming, even at night.

Lapwings tended to use wet fields, but beyond this there was no relationship with the extent of standing water, perhaps because a high water table, rather than standing water per se, is the important factor.

The overwhelming influence of standing water on wildfowl distribution, and associations between water levels and vegetation characteristics, made assessment of relationships between vegetation characteristics and wildfowl distribution difficult. There was some evidence that Wigeon made less use of fields with longer swards (average height over 7cm). Research elsewhere has shown that, by day, Wigeon favour short swards, but this association may be more marked in day-time, when they are tied to refuge pools and therefore repeatedly graze the adjacent swards. Lapwing were also found more often in fields with short swards when feeding at night.

Wigeon presence was lower in fields with abundant rush and sedge cover, perhaps because these species are unpalatable, or because the birds are more vulnerable to predators concealed in the cover. Fields with rush and sedge cover are used as roosts by Lapwing at night, and Snipe by day. No firm conclusions were drawn regarding the influence of vegetation on Teal distribution. However, the presence of rush and sedge species is thought to be beneficial for Teal and probably Shoveler, both as a source of seeds, and as a trap for floating food.

Opposite page: Lapwing. RW

Anecdotal observations suggested that Creeping Buttercup *Ranunculus repens* may be an important food plant for Wigeon and Bewick's Swan on the Levels and Moors. The latter species was thought to be responsible for accumulations of plants which had been uprooted in flooded fields, probably to eat the roots, which are rich in starch.

The numbers of Wigeon and Teal observed in the survey areas at night clearly indicate that nocturnal dispersal involves a substantial proportion of those present in refuges by day. In typical conditions (no flooding), it seems that most Wigeon and Teal feed mainly at night, using very shallow water which remains quite extensive and allows the Levels and Moors to sustain substantial populations of these species. Pintail and Shoveler are largely restricted to the refuge areas in these conditions. Day-time observations of wildfowl activity in the West Sedgemoor refuge area in winter 2001/02 indicated a low level of diurnal feeding, perhaps because the food supply is depleted in the refuge area. In species in which the energy value of their food is poor, some nocturnal feeding is a necessity. For example, it has been shown that Wigeon typically need to feed for 13 to 15 hours per day to meet their energy requirements in winter. However, research suggests that heavy reliance on nocturnal feeding reflects a lack of undisturbed sites suitable for day-time feeding.

The extensive disturbance-free habitat provided by flooding on the Somerset Levels and Moors creates optimum conditions for waterfowl, which can then feed by day as well as at night. Wetland Bird Survey (WeBS) counts show a striking correlation between high numbers of the key waterfowl species and periods of flooding. The often dramatic increase in waterfowl numbers on the Somerset Levels during flooding indicates a substantial influx of birds from well beyond the Somerset Levels. However, these conditions rarely persist for long. The floods are pumped away, and the wildfowl, having seemingly materialized from nowhere, 'vanish' again – returning to the refuges or leaving the area.

In a dry winter, such as 2001/02, even the shallow water used by birds feeding at night is in relatively short supply, and diurnal refuges are smaller. Food supplies may be depleted because of the concentrated distribution of wildfowl. Numbers of all key wildfowl species are much reduced in these conditions. The pressure on wildfowl in these conditions was evident in the dry early winter of 2001/02, when substantial numbers were feeding by day in the limited areas of shallow standing water available at the time, mainly in Raised Water Level Areas (RWLA). The higher Wigeon numbers recorded at night in this dry winter (Table 2), when numbers on the Levels were relatively low, were attributed to the over-representation of wet areas, including RWLAs, in the survey areas.

Swans at sunset.

Cygnets.

Lapwing on flooded moor.

An important aspect of the study was assessing the effect of habitat manipulation for key waterfowl species through the areas' status as an Environmentally Sensitive Area, especially the role of RWLAs. Bearing in mind the importance of standing water, it was encouraging to find that RWLAs were generally successful in providing much wetter conditions than elsewhere, though most of them are not sufficiently wet to hold wildfowl by day. On average, there were significantly more duck at night in RWLAs than elsewhere, except in the wet winter of 2000/01, when standing water was also widespread outside RWLAs. In the dry early winter of 2001/02, RWLAs, and some tier 2 fields, successfully retained surface water, which was otherwise very limited. Duck relied particularly heavily on RWLAs at this time, including during day-time, confirming the importance of these areas in dry periods. Lapwing were noted least frequently in RWLAs, but conditions suitable for this species are widespread.

Among the other factors potentially influencing night-time behaviour, there was some evidence that Teal and Lapwing dispersal was reduced on nights with moderate or severe frost, and on dark nights (i.e. close to new moon). Teal may be most widespread and active on nights around the full moon. My impression was that wildfowl were less vocal on dark nights, perhaps because they are more vulnerable to predators in such conditions. Interestingly, we walked to within 30 m of two small flocks of Wigeon – and retreated without flushing them - on King's Sedgemoor on a dark, windy night in January 2003, which would not have been possible on a moonlit night. There was also anecdotal evidence that Wigeon distribution is more concentrated during frosts.

There were, of course, unexpected observations during the three winters of night survey. In all three winters, Coots were heard flying overhead on occasions, always in late winter (late January onwards). It was rarely possible to determine the direction of flight, but it was suspected that these birds were flying north or north-east, suggesting they were migrants. Alternatively, they may have been exploring for feeding sites - late winter floods on the Levels can attract moderate numbers of Coots. This night-time aerial activity is perhaps not surprising in a species which would be very vulnerable to avian predators by day.

Thrushes, especially Redwings and Fieldfares, were frequently flushed from roost-sites in bushes beside droves, but much less expected was the discovery that these species will feed at night. On several occasions on brightly moonlit nights, we encountered unidentified thrushes apparently feeding in fields.

Swan and cygnet.

Wet Woodland of the Levels and Moors

Tony Serjeant

The Levels and Moors landscape is not renowned for its trees. True, the area's characteristic willow pollards are justly famous, yet woodland as such is not a common habitat on the inland Moors and is even less abundant on the coastal Levels.

In striking contrast to the essentially treeless expanse of the Levels and Moors, extensive, mature woodlands clothe large areas of the limestone ridges and of the hills that surround the low lying land. Many of these hillside and escarpment woodlands are ancient in character and have been designated as important conservation sites, several being managed as flagship nature reserves, such as Aller and Beer Woods. In the Levels and Moors, where a premium is placed on open habitats that support breeding waders and wintering flocks of waterfowl, most conservationists regard the development of scrub and woodland as a trend to be resisted.

It is often said that woodland is the 'natural' state of most of lowland England that would establish eventually were humans to stop managing the land. There are relatively few places where the experiment has been carried out to see just what does happen when human intervention ceases. One site where the consequences have been monitored closely over a lengthy period of time is Sharpham Moor Plot. The plants on this tiny parcel of peatland, two miles west of Glastonbury, have been studied since 1915. In the early 1920s botanists bought the site to study how the vegetation would change with time once grazing was removed. A mere twenty years later the whole plot had become 'carr' woodland. 'Carr' is a general term for woodland on land with a high water table on which thrive trees that are tolerant of wet conditions such as willows, birch and alder.

GR

Top: Fen-marsh at Westhay.

Above: Fly Agaric at Sharpham Moor plot, under birch.

Were it not for human intervention, the Levels and Moors would certainly have a far greater coverage of trees today. There is plenty of evidence in the peat that the Levels and Moors was a much more wooded landscape at various times in the past than it is today. The peat that formed 5500 years ago is choked with tree roots, dead branches, twigs and leaves, indicating that an extensive wet forest cloaked much of the peat moors. In some places, conditions became so dry as to allow Ash, oak and elm to flourish in the place of the carr species. The pollen records show how this once-extensive prehistoric woodland came to be reduced enormously, firstly by agriculture and later, as the climate became much wetter, by the spread of huge, desolate expanses of bog. Tree cover on the Levels and Moors has fluctuated over the centuries since the great prehistoric 'high forest' - woodland periodically reclaiming drier areas of land abandoned by farmers in adverse times only to retreat once more as agricultural fortunes change and the land is cleared again or wetter conditions prevail once more.

At certain times in history the wet woodland itself (or rather the timber it produced) was a prized commodity. Medieval documents record the presence of extensive natural alder beds in the Sowy Moors, around Street, Walton and South Moors and in eastern Queen's Sedgemoor. Such beds were primarily exploited for firewood, very few people being allowed the right to take timber for construction purposes. These rights were jealously guarded and there are accounts of violence and arson following the unauthorised felling of trees at Meare in 1299. These incidents appear to have been part of a long-running feud between the Bishops of Wells and the Abbots of Glastonbury concerning ownership of properties in the Brue valley! The records demonstrate that some blocks of wet woodland had significant economic value in the past. This contrasts with the present day where the habitat tends to be regarded as of little value and a sign of poor management and neglect.

The main concentration of woodland on the Levels and Moors today is in the Brue valley. Here small wooded blocks are to be found typically on land that has been cut for peat and left to vegetate over. Many of the woods that have grown up on these peat cuttings have a primaeval, unmanaged appearance; yet, none of these woods can be described as 'ancient' in the sense that there has been more or less continuous tree cover for hundreds of years. In ecological terms they are recent habitats and for this reason it is often assumed that they are bound to be of less conservation interest than the larger, more ancient woodlands of the higher ground. This is to underestimate their worth to wildlife.

Judgements about the conservation value of a wood are often based upon the quality of the ground flora it supports. Few woods on the Levels and Moors can boast the attractive array of wildflowers

Fen carr Shapwick. DB

OTTERS

The Somerset Levels and Moors have long been quoted as a 'stronghold' for the Otter.

Although Somerset's Otters suffered decline due to pesticides and habitat loss, much as they did throughout Southern Britain, they can still be seen and recorded throughout the area.

Over the past years, sightings of Otters from hides on the Somerset Levels Reserves have become a regular highlight. However, the future of our Otters is by no means secure and they face many difficulties. Pollution, increasing traffic and new diseases will always pose threats.

The Somerset Otter Group monitors Otter presence on a regular basis. English Nature, the RSPB and the Environment Agency work hard together to do all that they can to ensure the future of this charismatic and popular creature.

Russell Gomm

Otter swimming and juvenile on bank.

that carpets many of the ancient woodland sites in Spring and early Summer. Indeed, the floor of many wet woods is often blanketed by common, little-regarded species such as Nettle and Bramble.

However, this is not to say that all the area's wet woodlands are devoid of any plant species of interest. Among these woods one can still encounter the majestic Royal Fern, and its more delicate relative the Marsh Fern. Milk Parsley, the food plant of the spectacular Swallowtail butterfly, is a wet woodland equivalent of the commoner roadside and hedgerow Cow Parsley. One of the most striking inhabitants of the wettest woods is the Greater Tussock Sedge, its robust tussocks reminiscent of suburban Pampas Grass. The wet woods are particularly rich in fungi, mosses and liverworts – groups of organisms that in the past have tended to be lumped together, rather condescendingly, as 'lower plants'.

Among the birds that are associated with the Levels and Moors carr woodlands are the Nightingale, the Grasshopper Warbler and the Cetti's Warbler. The latter species is widely distributed across Europe and Asia but, until 1972, it had never been observed to breed in this country. Many sites on the Levels and Moors now have breeding populations and its startling and very distinctive outburst of song is now almost commonplace in locations with scrubby, damp habitats and reed-bed – a sign almost certainly of recent milder winters and, possibly, of global warming.

The presence of relatively large amounts of standing deadwood makes the wet woodlands ideal places to look for Great Spotted Woodpecker and its less common relative, the Lesser Spotted Woodpecker. Among the more secretive inhabitants of the drier 'wet' woods are Woodcock and in a few places where woodland or scrub mingles with heath, Nightjar. Sadly, the Willow Tit, a wet woodland counterpart of the more familiar garden Coal Tit, is no longer believed to breed on the Levels and Moors.

The most conspicuous of all animals to be found on the Levels and Moors is the Roe Deer. Often seen in the open countryside during the day, it rests at night in the small blocks of woodland that are dotted within the landscape. Surprisingly, given the often- waterlogged ground conditions, Badgers make their homes in the wet woodlands and their setts are a common feature of many Levels and Moors woods. Otters also may use small blocks of dense carr and wet scrub as places in which to hide and rest during the day.

Blushing Bracket
Daedaleopsis confragosa.

Roe Deer.

In terms of the flora and fauna it supports, the wet woodland of the Somerset Levels and Moors is probably most important for its invertebrate life. It is only relatively recently that it began to be realised just how important the habitat could be both in terms of county and of national conservation objectives for invertebrate conservation. Analysis of invertebrate records shows that the Levels and Moors support an unexpectedly high number of rare and threatened invertebrates many of which are usually associated with old growth, ancient woodland. It seems anomalous that a habitat that has established only relatively recently should be so rich in ancient woodland species, yet such findings are explicable when it is realised that the wet woodlands share some features in common with ancient woodlands that make them highly attractive to certain invertebrate groups. They contain relatively large volumes of dead wood and rotting matter encouraging the flies and beetles that specialise in making a living from these materials. The abundance of fungi and mosses favours those invertebrates that feed or live in these. The presence of ancient woodland on the nearby hills and ridges means that there has been a source from which ancient woodland specialist invertebrates could colonise the relatively new woods. Finally, it should be remembered that many of the woods that have grown up on old peat cuttings have escaped intensive management, such as regular coppicing, removal of dead wood, etc that has been employed in other lowland woods to the detriment of species that rely on old-growth forest.

As well as the ancient woodland specialists there is also a whole suite of rare invertebrates associated with the area's wet woodlands that rely on particular conditions that are particularly prevalent in wet woods. For example, in order to breed successfully, the Lesser Silver Water Beetle *Hydrocara caraboides*, requires shaded water with plenty of submerged leaf litter to attract prey for its carnivorous grub to feed upon – conditions that it finds in abundance in the pools and wet hollows inside dense wet woodland.

In conclusion, the wet woodland of the Somerset Levels and Moors makes a very important contribution to the area's overall biodiversity. Only recently has this begun to be appreciated. Conservation priorities for the Levels and Moors area may still need some adjustment in order to take account of our developing new understanding of the importance of the habitat.

WETLANDS
WHAT FUTURE?

Isle of Avalon from flooded worked-out peat diggings.

Unique, Unrivalled and Disappearing – What hope for Somerset's wetland heritage?

Richard Brunning

Our knowledge of the prehistoric period on the moors has been directed by forces largely beyond the control of archaeologists. Finding archaeological sites deeply buried in water-logged peat is extremely difficult. The normal techniques of fieldwalking to retrieve artefacts, examining aerial photographs for crop marks and using geophysical surveys are all poorly suited to such environments.

Because the Somerset moors have not suffered from the extensive ploughing of other major wetlands such as the Fens, the main avenue for exploring the hidden wetland heritage has been in the areas of peat cutting in the central Brue valley. Peat cutting in these areas has been going on since Roman times but the first recorded discoveries of archaeology occur in the early 19th century by the Reverend W. Stradling.

The Brue valley and the peat cutting areas within it have remained the centre of archaeological investigation until the beginning of the present century. As a result our knowledge of the other moors is far more limited but the evidence available suggests that they have the same potential. If the density of archaeological finds in the peat cutting areas is replicated elsewhere then our existing knowledge represents just the tip of the iceberg. Very little excavation has been carried out on the other moors so if sites are being slowly destroyed by gradual desiccation they are passing with no record being made before their extinction.

The waterlogged archaeology on the moors has characteristics of composition, preservation and vulnerability, which separate it from the wider body of the archaeological resource. Because of the anaerobic conditions present in waterlogged environments, the normal processes of decay do not occur. The result is that organic materials such as wood and leather often survive in good condition. Such survival is of immense archaeological importance because the organic component formed the largest part of the material culture of all societies from the prehistoric to the medieval period.

In addition, environmental information, in the form of pollen, plant remains, coleoptera, snails, foraminifera, and diatoms, often also survives in waterlogged deposits. Analysis of these remains allows archaeologists to reconstruct the changing local landscape over thousands of years and see how it responded to sea level and climate change and how people began to use and adapt it.

The wealth of information available from wetland sites can be seen in the example of the Sweet Track. This structure and its associated palaeoenvironmental data have generated a vast amount of information about the early Neolithic period when the first settled farming human communities were being established.

The environmental remains provide information on the local and regional scale. Beetle remains show that early Neolithic Somerset experienced a significantly different climate from today, more akin to present day Denmark with hotter summers and colder winters. Pollen and plant remains show how the wetland landscape was changing in response to sea level rise. These changes may have triggered the need for the trackway to be built.

Pollen evidence shows how the dryland forests were beginning to be gradually cleared, by the creation of clearings that only lasted a few years. The wood from the trackway itself shows the huge scale of the long-lived trees from this primary forest and how man was gradually changing its character.

A vast array of artefacts were found beside the track, some accidental losses and some seemingly offering to the Gods of the wetlands. These range from pottery and wooden bowls to axes, bows and small items such as wooden stirrers, remains of arrowshafts and yew pins. It forms our most complete picture of the material culture of the first farmers. New analysis is discovering more, such as lipid remains extracted from the pottery that provide the earliest evidence for dairying in the UK. Tree-ring dating from the oak planks used in the track has enabled a precision of dating that is

BOTH PHOTOGRAPHS RB

unimaginable on normal archaeological sites. We know that an initial track (the Post Track) was formed in **3838 BC**, that the Sweet Track itself was built over the winter of **3807 to 3806 BC** and that its was repaired for at least **6** years thereafter.

How important is Somerset's wetland heritage in a national context? Many of the UK's extensive wetland areas have been heavily damaged by agriculture and or peat extraction. Arable agriculture in the Humber wetlands and the Fens has destroyed countless waterlogged archaeological sites. By contrast the Somerset peat moors are fortunate that peat extraction has been limited to one area, and that pasture rather than arable farming has been the norm.

This essential difference means that the Somerset moors probably have comparatively better preservation of waterlogged sites than any other extensive wetland area in the UK. The importance of Somerset's prehistoric wetland heritage can be shown by a few basic facts;

- 25% of all the prehistoric waterlogged sites thought still to exist in England are from the Somerset moors
- The wetland prehistoric trackways and settlements deemed worthy of Scheduled Monument status in England all occur in Somerset

Above left: Bog oaks from a Bronze Age forest, removed from a field near Athelney during the installation of under drainage

Above right: The Late Bronze Age ritual pile alignment at Harter's Hill, Queen's Sedgemoor, where peat wastage has reduced the ground surface to the tops of the oak piles.

- The County Museum in Taunton Castle holds the largest collection of conserved prehistoric worked wood in the UK, possibly in the whole of Europe
- The Sweet Track and Glastonbury lake village have produced our most complete record of Neolithic and Iron Age material culture ever discovered in the UK
- Glastonbury lake village is the best preserved prehistoric settlement ever discovered in the UK
- Queen's Sedgemoor contains the longest lowland peat sequence in England

The Somerset Moors have the most important prehistoric wetland archaeology in the UK but how well is this heritage surviving today? There is relatively little threat from development such as road and house building although the edges of the floodplain are being encroached upon, for example around Glastonbury and Bridgwater.

The extent of peat extraction in the county has reduced considerably in the last two decades as large areas of land have gone out of production, often to become part of new nature reserves. Extraction is continuing with no end date in sight and an increasing percentage of the central Brue valley is destined for such open cast mining. The effect on wetland archaeology can largely be mitigated through the planning process although there are difficulties, most notably in methodologies for identifying sites in deep peat and in the ability of small local peat firms to meet the large cost of excavating waterlogged remains if they are discovered during extraction.

By far the biggest threat comes from peat wastage. This is because it is a far more extensive threat than other pressures. In addition it lies outside the planning process so it is impossible to finance mitigation through the 'polluter pays' principle.

What is peat wastage? When peat is drained large amounts of water are lost and oxygen is introduced allowing the organic matter to be decayed by micro-organisms. This results in the shrinkage of the peat as it literally wastes away. In arable fields 1cm to 2cm is lost annually and many arable fields on the moors have become so low that they can now no longer be farmed conventionally.

Even in pasture fields there is often poor summer irrigation and over a century 50cm to 75cm of peat can be lost. This seems quite slow but is enough to destroy all the known wetland Scheduled Monuments in Somerset.

Opposite page:
Wetland under water. LN

THE SOMERSET WETLANDS, A THREATENED LANDSCAPE: SOME HISTORICAL QUOTATIONS

AD 878: *'So inaccessible on account of bogs and inundation of lakes that it cannot be approached but by boat'.*
William of Malmesbury's description of Athelney based on Asser's contemporary account.

Mid 14th century: *'Under water in winter.'*
Kingsmoor in the Yeo valley. Inquisition 'Post Mortem', 1353-5.

1507: *'If this marsh wall were not kept ... all the plan [flat] marsh ground at sudden rains would be overflowed [flooded].'*
Leland's diary, describing the bank on the South side of Hartlake River and just North of Glastonbury.

1607: *'In a short time did whole villages stand like islands (compassed around with water), and in a more short time were those islands undis-coverable and nowhere to be found. The tops of trees and houses only appeared...'*
An anonymous broadsheet describing all the moors North of the Polden Hills (see separate item for more details).

Early 17th Century: *'Often times at high and spring tides, the sea water, both surrounded and encompassed the houses, and both floors... '*
Records of drainage work on the northern Levels.

1655: *'The waste is boggy and unwholesome, but could be improved by draining.'*
Drainage engineer, Vermuyden, describing Kings Sedgemoor.

1663: *'So covered with water you would rather deem them sea than land.'*
The moors North and South of Langport.

'In the winter time most covered over with water'.
The moors of the Tone valley.
Both from Gerard of Trent's 'Descriptions of Somerset'.

1747: *, ... subject to floods and dangerous inundations.'*
The road from Bridgwater to Bristol, in Defoe's *A Tour through the whole island of Great Britain*.

1771: *'In winter it is a sea ...'*
King's Sedgemoor, from *'A Farmer's Tour ...'* by Young.

1775: *'A morass by reason of the waters standing on it ...'*
King's Sedgemoor, from the Journals of the House of Commons.

1780: *, ... in wet winters people have been known to come from the Parrett in boats to the very doors'* (of houses in Somerton).
The King's Sedgemoor area, in *A Tour through part of England, Scotland and Wales*.

1798: *'Frequent inundation and sometimes in rainy seasons - covered with water for four or five successive months.'*
The moors North of the western Mendip Hills.

View from Burrowbridge towards Athelney and East Lyng.

1798: '... *stagnant waters and unwholesome air.'*
The moors in general.
Both descriptions from Billingsley's *A General View of the Agriculture of Somerset.*

1800 : *'One wide sheet of water spread itself over the flats* [moors] *...'*
The Brue valley. in Warner's 'A Walk through some of the Western Counties of England'.

1852: *'Completely under water ...'*
The Parrett valley. from a report for the Royal Agricultural Society.

l870s: ' *... exceedingly wet and ill-drained, as well as liable to ruinous inundation.'*
Moors North and South of Langport. the 'Journal of the Bath and West of England Society'.

1919: *'... flood regularly or are permanently water-logged.'*
The Brue valley and southern moors. in Report to the Board of Agriculture on the Drainage of the valleys of the Parrett, Tone, Cary. Brue and Axe.

1929*: 'It was not uncommon for certain villages and hamlets to be isolated during flood periods ... children had been unable to get to school for weeks at a time.'*
Newspaper report of a general Somerset drainage conference in Bridgwater.

DB

1981: *'Between five and six thousand acres of farmland are under several feet of water ...'*
North Sedgemoor; the *Bridgwater Mercury* newspaper.

2000: *'For three weeks land in Sedgemoor and stretching towards Taunton has been submerged under millions of gallons of water.'*
The *Bridgwater Times.*

2001: *'... the Tone and Parrett ... both burst their banks during mass flooding ...'*
Sedgemoor; the *Bridgwater Times.*

2001: *'... extra money ... will be used to improve flood defences to try to prevent a repeat of this year's flooding disasters ...'*
Report on multi-million pound project; the *Bridgwater Times*

Jean Pilgrim, Derek Briggs

Above: One of the Neolithic Chilton brushwood trackways being sampled to assess its condition

Above left: The Neolithic Abbot's Way track in a very poor state of preservation due to desiccation.

Left: Hydrological monitoring on part of the Sweet Track, using piezometers and redox probes.

Far left: A more sustainable farming regime – high summer water levels on the South Drain upstream of Gold Corner.

What is the present condition of the wetland heritage? It is not easy to assess the condition of water-logged archaeological structures. For over 99% of such sites thought to survive *in situ* in the UK we have no accurate information on their present condition. Excavation to expose the remains and monitoring of the local hydrological regime are both required to determine the condition of the monument and the threats to its preservation.

The Somerset Levels Project assessed the condition of some of the monuments they discovered, but hydrological monitoring was only undertaken over part of the Sweet Track in Shapwick Heath. Up till 2004 there was only recent information on the condition of a 500m length of the Sweet Track, a short stretch of the Neolithic Abbots Way and two recently investigated Bronze Age ritual sites at Greylake and Harter's Hill. Elsewhere in the UK there was comparable information from half a dozen rural prehistoric wetland sites.

To address this lack of information English Heritage, Somerset County Council and the Environment Agency funded the Monuments At Risk In Somerset's Peatlands (MARISP) project. This has assessed the condition of eleven nationally important wetland sites. The assessment comprised limited excavation to recover samples to determine the condition of wood structural remains and associated palaeoenvironmental deposits (pollen, plant macrofossils, beetles, snails and diatoms). The other component was a year of hydrological monitoring and analysis of water quality.

Of the eleven sites examined, two (Vipers and Nidons Bronze Age trackways) appear to have been totally destroyed by ploughing, despite the supposed protection of Scheduled Monument status. This is consistent with the experience of the Skinners Wood trackways, also of Bronze Age date, that have been largely destroyed by arable farming and peat extraction c.1 km further west in the valley.

The other nine sites are all in permanent pasture but are suffering from desiccation in the summer months with the exception of Glastonbury Lake Village which appears to be in a naturally wetter hydrological regime, possibly because of its proximity to a former channel of the River Brue. The condition of the surviving monuments is very variable. At the Iron Age settlement of Meare Lake Village wooden remains have virtually ceased to exist because of the low ground water levels. The Neolithic Bell and Abbot's Way tracks are also suffering severely and are quite close to the ground surface. The wooden remains at most of the other sites are still in a condition where a lot of information can still be extracted but seasonal desiccation is annually diminishing this information.

Of all the wetland sites in the Somerset moors the present information suggests that there is optimism for the long-term survival of only two sites. One of these, the Sweet Track in Shapwick Heath NNR, is protected by an irrigation system operated by English Nature. The other site, Glastonbury Lake Village, is protected by a capping of silt and appears to be in a naturally wetter hydrological regime. All the other known sites are dying a slow death from desiccation and some have already died. The only remaining uncertainty is the speed of the dying process.

Is there a sustainable future? Numerous studies have been conducted on the sustainable management of peat soils. One local study has provided the baseline conditions that are required to avoid wastage of peat soils. This suggested maximum spacing of irrigation features of 40 m to 60 m depending on soil permeability, and ground water tables that do not fall below 50 cm from the ground surface in summer.

These conditions are only coming close to being met in some very limited areas, most notably in the Raised Water Level Areas (RWLA's) financed through the Environmentally Sensitive Area (ESA) scheme and in some land managed by the RSPB on West Sedgemoor and Shapwick allotment at Greinton. For the rest of the moors slow peat wastage is the norm although the position should be slightly better in the SSSI areas where there is greater control over the summer water penning arrangements.

A new agri-environment scheme, Environmental Stewardship, replaced the ESA scheme in 2005. It is unrealistic to expect the new scheme to deliver a sudden solution to the problem. It is likely that the achievement of favourable and sustainable condition of both the natural and archaeological wetland heritage of the moors will require a more radical change in the existing farming and water management practice. Vast amounts of public money are being spent in the area through flood and water management by the Environment Agency and through DEFRA's other wings of the Rural Development Service, who administer the agri-environment schemes, and English Nature. More radical thinking within DEFRA may be required to achieve sustainable land management on the moors and a safe future for the internationally important natural and archaeological wetland heritage.

Roe deer between peat blocks, Sharpham Triangle. GR

Farming on the Levels and Moors – Past, present and future challenges

Peter Beeden

The Levels and Moors covers some 245 square miles (635 km2 or 63 455 ha) within the middle of Somerset where the flood risk, water table level and soil type determine the type of farming that can take place. The Levels refers mainly to those areas where peat is covered with clay, whereas the Moors have mainly peat to the ground surface. Currently, some 235 square miles (609 km^2 or 60 865 ha) of the whole area is less than 10 m above sea level, with 40% of this at less than 5 m above sea level.

Drainage of the Levels and Moors started in the 12th century, coinciding with an extended period of dry and warm weather. Open field systems were then normal with villagers providing ploughing and land cultivation services mainly for the Church. With the dissolution of the monasteries in the 16th century, the yeoman class was established, as land was sold to freeholders and private estates. By the 17th century, rotations became normal practice, with a balance of land under arable crops or grassland for beef, sheep and dairy cattle, and natural woodland was destroyed to make room for more cultivation. Drainage was accelerated in the 1700s and 1800s, to increase the period of the year when grazing stock would not be flooded out or merely damage the wet ground. Nevertheless, the supply of water in rhynes and drainage channels was vital even then for both stock drinking and for wet fencing, in lieu of the hedges that had been established elsewhere on drier ground, so as to keep grazing stock within a defined area. By the 18th century, lime and potash applications were introduced which, together with applications of farm yard manure, helped raise food production, complemented by innovations such as the introduction of new crops including turnips and swedes, gradual replacement of draught oxen with horses with iron instead of wooden ploughs, and new rotations including the Norfolk 4-course of wheat/barley and grass, but with no fallow period.

Then the introduction of the railway network in the 1800s increasingly enabled fresh farm produce to reach the growing urban communities that followed the Industrial Revolution, and the value of milk rose in the south-west. Pumping systems were introduced in the early 1900s for the purposes of flood evacuation and these were further refined during the 1950s-1970s so that farm systems became ever more dependent upon the land drainage systems. By the 1930s, the system of quickly transporting milk by rail to fulfil urban demand was well established and the economic depression and the general unprofitability of other agricultural products encouraged more farmers to divert to milk production. In most of the Levels and Moors, cattle were transported from their winter dry and higher ground to the outlying land that was usually wet in winter and were grazed there, being milked by hand until their return to the drier ground in the autumn. From the 1920s a portable milking parlour, known as a milking bail, was introduced; these had an engine that powered the vacuum pump for the milking machine. These bails enabled the operation of a more efficient milking process with a reduced labour requirement. Increasingly, the Levels and Moors became known for the production of milk transported to Bristol and London, and for cheese. Dairying continued as the main enterprise on the Levels and Moors until the dairy herds increased beyond the size suitable for milking within these small, albeit towable, milking bails.

Cattle in early morning mist at North Curry Moor.

Over many years, the Levels and Moors has been renowned for the production of withies and the pollarding of willows for basket making as a major source of employment for local people. This industry reached a peak in the 1930s and has continued until the present day, although the ever increasing cost of labour and competition from cheap imports and plastic-derived materials over the last 30-40 years has reduced it to a fraction of its former size. Increasingly, following the disbandment of the open field system, each individual Levels and Moors farm has become a widely scattered range of fields. There are those with dry, upper ground around the farm buildings on the edge of the moor, where grazing is possible in both early and late season, and others with fields in border ground on the edge of the Levels and Moors which are above most winter and spring flooding. Other fields will contribute rougher grazing on the lower ground that makes up most of the Moor and which is more liable to flooding in winter and occasionally in summer.

Dairy herd at Nyland Hill.

Even fewer farms on the Levels and Moors are now within a single block of land than was the practice in the past when less intensively managed. The area remains less well known than previously for its milk production and more now for beef and sheep production. Withy and willow growing for basket making continues, albeit on a small scale, as does arable crop production in better drained land. The initiation of the Somerset Levels Environmental Stewardship Area (ESA) scheme, has encouraged the management of land for wildlife as well as farm production. Under the Somerset Levels and Moors ESA farmers are paid to manage their land in certain ways so as to maintain and enhance its suitability primarily for the wildfowl and waders that migrate there in winter, together with those that remain to breed and the very wide range of wetland plants, insects and other invertebrates typical of the habitat. Although land is still used by dairy farmers, the generally low quality grass produced by the poor soils is suitable for grazing by young stock, dry cows and beef cattle rather than actively milking cows. In some areas sheep remain important, although invariably associated with drier land.

The ESA agri-environment scheme agreement is now an important component within farm businesses on the Levels and Moors, with payments from the Department of Environment, Food and Rural Affairs (DEFRA) for managing land in specified ways. So, for example, payments are made for permanent grassland which, during the ten-year agreement period, will receive only specified maximum fertiliser levels which qualifies for £125 per ha each year, whilst about 1 800 ha of land, that is splash-flooded over winter and subsequently grazed at low stocking rates or with a late hay crop taken in July, qualifies for £430 per ha.

With the replacement of area and headage payments designed to support agriculture under the Integrated Administration and Control System (IACS) and by the introduction of the Single Payment Scheme, 2005 has been a year of great change in UK agriculture. Many farmers are concerned over their future and are still unsure of what these changes will mean for their farm businesses and future land management. This has been complicated by the simultaneous launch of the Environmental Stewardship Scheme to replace the Countryside Stewardship and ESA Schemes.

In the short-term, a major impact on the Levels and Moors of this change in the support mechanism to farming which bases payments to individual farmers on historical levels rather than the number of stock or area of crop managed, could be of major significance to land areas such as the Levels and Moors which, for reasons of high water table and the risks of winter and occasionally summer flooding, do not readily lend themselves to the high level of productivity necessary to operate efficiently a commercial farming business. Before 2005, and in order to avoid over-grazing and possible overuse of inorganic fertiliser regimes in areas such as the Levels and Moors, with potential leaching of nutrients into the water supply systems, farmers throughout UK have been able to claim 'extensification payments' when suckler cows and beef cattle stocking densities were maintained at low levels.

Bee.

Above: Ploughing for swamp rice is never easy and the use of buffalo like these in Java used to 'poach' the flooded ground before transplanting seedlings could become an important way of life on the Levels and Moors.

Top right: Subsistence farmers' houses on stilts at the edge of their growing swamp rice like these in Java, could become a familiar site on the Levels and Moors following global warming.

Right: Could these rice terraces with banana and coconut become the norm on the Levels and Moors as global warming develops? (This picture was taken in Java)

The additional land required to enable the low stocking densities of less than 1.4 Livestock Units per ha to be achieved, and the additional payment to be claimed, has often been found on the Levels and Moors. But, with this incentive to manage large areas of land extensively removed, there is the possibility that the least productive land in areas such as the Levels and Moors may fall out of regular agricultural usage and, were there to be no grazing at all, may revert to scrub development and eventually to secondary woodland. It would seem inevitable that the land most peripheral to commercial farming could readily revert to willow carr and remain ungrazed in the future.

The effects of these recent changes in institutional support for the agricultural sector remain unclear and may become exacerbated, or indeed minimised, by evolving social and global conditions. For example, food costs now contribute a lower proportion of monthly take-home pay for the average salaried person than perhaps ever before, but, were the oil price rises seen in 2005 to be maintained or exceeded, then the cost of imported food materials from countries far afield would have to rise to cover transport costs. This could put UK farmers in a better position to compete and slow down the reduction in the numbers of farmers which has occurred in recent years. It would also reduce the need for growth in individual farm size which has been necessary to maintain a reasonable standard of farm income. This, together with the currently emerging demand for locally produced food, as shown by the increased popularity of Farmers' Markets, accompanied by a greater willingness of producers to participate, may result in more substantial prices being paid for UK agricultural produce. This should, in turn, encourage existing farm production with perhaps even an enhanced level with the new entrants to the farming world.

Secondary woodland.

In the medium to longer term, changes in weather patterns caused by the 'global warming' process are likely to influence the type of agriculture possible on the Levels and Moors to an even greater extent. Current thinking on the impacts of global warming suggest that there is likely to be a substantial rise in the occurrence of extreme weather, whether heavy rainfall events, prolonged dry periods, or even lengthy cold periods. More obvious probable changes would result from sea level rises, predicted to be up to 1.8 m by the end of the 21st century or, with melting of giant land-based ice sheets such as the one covering West Antarctica, as much as 5 m.

The general rise in temperatures that would cause such projected increases in sea levels, would have substantial impacts on potential future enterprises and land productivity of the Levels and Moors. Temperature rises are likely to be throughout the year, rather than reflected merely during the

RW

summer months. Although the range of harsh and mild winters is likely to continue, the relative severity of these is likely to be reduced dramatically, with less frost and prolonged ice events, than occur at present. Plant growing seasons are likely to be extended substantially too, probably with grass growth throughout the year, albeit at a reduced level during the winter months. On the Levels and Moors this would be both beneficial in drier winters and on slightly elevated ground, but detrimental perhaps on the more low lying areas that are not flooded. This is because the incremental grass growth might be difficult to harvest and remove for zero-grazing of cattle, or even to allow grazing by cattle or sheep without substantial damage to the ground surface. The overall effect; however, is the extension of the grazing season from the current 220-250 days per year to 300 days or even more.

A downside of this anticipated temperature rise would be an increase in the burning off or 'scorching' of grass swards in dry hot summers, particularly on the more elevated areas of the Levels and Moors where there is a lower water table. Perennial ryegrass breeding programmes would need to focus on the selection of new varieties able to resist such damage, and graziers might even have to return to the development of grass swards rich in Cock's-foot, a grass with deep rooting habit that can resist drought conditions! Elsewhere on the Levels and Moors, the frequently high water table during the growing season may confer some advantage during drought periods, enabling a greater productivity than possible on better drained land.

These temperature rises could also influence the crops that could be grown. Nationally, crop introductions have become commonplace, although mainly as a result of changes in farming systems and requirements rather than climate change. Maize for example was almost entirely unknown as a fodder crop for livestock until the mid-1960s and oilseed rape only became a familiar yellow landmark in the countryside in the 1970s; both are now widespread. Elephant Grass *Miscanthus,* a native plant of Africa and Asia, has been grown increasingly over the past 10 years for animal bedding, energy use and a range of other purposes. The use of the Levels and Moors for short rotation coppice, mainly of willow but perhaps also of *Miscanthus,* could become a greater priority were oil prices to continue to rise without the use of renewable energy. With its water store, prevailing westerly winds, and the proximity of the Severn Estuary, the potential for development of power alternatives for areas within or near the Somerset Levels and Moors of heat exchange systems, wind, solar, and tidal flow power is great.

With relatively small increases in summer temperatures, farming in areas of the Levels and Moors has the potential for different cropping patterns. High water tables could become appropriate for the production of paddy rice, given varietal selection amongst the japonica types that are particularly cold tolerant. Rice is already grown in Italy, southern France, Russia, Missouri State in USA and in areas such as northern Vietnam, which are known for cold winters, and to latitude 50° North. Rice lacks tolerance to saline conditions however, and perhaps genetic modification for its survival in those conditions, already being undertaken by international research organisations for tropical irrigation schemes, would be necessary before it could be grown in areas liable to sea water inundation. Paddy rice requires controlled in-field water depths of no greater than 0.4 metre and which must be reduced prior to harvest as the crop ripens. Deep water rice able to produce rapid stem elongation as water levels rise is also possible, but these varieties have a lower yield than paddy rice. For both types, control dams and sluices would be essential and these would need to be complemented by a tidal barrier (another power source!) on the River Parrett itself, so as to avoid excessive inundation inland. It would also enable controlled irrigation practice where required, complemented by a re-focussed pumping programme designed to maintain water levels only where they are necessary. The temperatures and damp conditions which would enable swamp rice to be grown would also favour a range of tropical crops, including banana, which likes damp conditions and is grown in the Canary Islands, irrigated cotton and crops such as soya beans, navy beans for baked beans, grain maize and flax.

The changes in grass swards, which would occur naturally if water tables were to rise and grassland become wetter, would inevitably be less nutrient rich and therefore less productive for grazing livestock. Sedges, reed and rushes would predominate in wetter areas and effective grazing would be achieved only by extensive grazing with native breeds of beef cattle and, to a lesser extent, sheep which can grow and finish on poor quality forage. Indeed, one option might be the expansion of the water buffalo population, recently introduced into UK for the production of mozzarella type cheese, but in this case for meat production. Even with smaller sea level rises, because the Levels and Moors are only marginally above mean sea level, it may well develop into areas of almost permanent inland water as water tables rise. This may prevent traditional farming from being undertaken in those areas, although inland fish farming would likely become an attractive enterprise as the world's human population increases and both freshwater and sea fish population decline with over exploitation. Fish species would vary according to water salinity, depth and available aquatic vegetation, and although populations might be initiated with rainbow trout, could later include other freshwater fish such as carp and bream, or even to sea trout and salmon.

PB

Perhaps banana growing like this in Uganda might be seen on the Levels and Moors in future?

Opposite page: Bittern, well disguised in reeds by its black-streaked brown plumage.

199

Fishing in the rivers and rhynes crossing the Levels and Moors has been normal practice for generations both for local consumption and export to urban areas. Elver fishing is perhaps most widely known, although for anglers freshwater fish such as Roach, Rudd, Bream, Tench, Pike and occasional Grass Carp are the main attractions. Were a Severn Estuary or a River Parrett Barrages not to be constructed, then, with substantial rises in sea levels following an extended period of global warming, an inland sea would develop over much of the Levels and Moors. This Somerset Sea would increase in area as mean sea levels rose and would be subject to normal tidal events. Fish populations would change to reflect increased salinity with a rising proportion of Salmon and Sea Trout as well as incursion of Bass, Herring, Sprats and Shad.

With the barrage construction, then the possibility of inland and freshwater lakes on the Levels and Moors should not be ruled out. Assuming that rainfall levels were maintained then the freshwater fish described above would thrive. With increasing temperatures then other fish species might be introduced in the same way that the massive Nile Perch was introduced to Lake Victoria in Central Africa and subsequently destroyed much of the local fish population! With the development of inland sea or freshwater lakes then fishing would increase, initially perhaps purely for pleasure angling but perhaps later for commercial purposes. If the scenario of energy limitation were to be realised, then smallholder fishermen with canoes or small boats with oars or paddles, might catch fish to sell to the local people, just as is the norm throughout most of Africa and Asia!

These prognostications are made assuming a continuation of the UK socio-economic conditions as at the beginning of the 21st century, with only a very small proportion of the nation's population actively involved in agriculture, both food and industrial crop production. It could be speculated that further population increase and the impact of shortage of oil together with rises in the market cost of energy from whatever source, could stimulate a return to the land by families or communities in order to produce their own food requirements. Under such circumstances it could be argued that the Levels and Moors, with the potential for producing a wide range of food, fibre for clothing and fuel for cooking and heating, could be an extremely valuable resource for those able to secure access to land there – unless, of course, it is completely under the sea!

PB

Might the use of coracles for fishing, as seen here in Wales, become normal practice on the Levels and Moors?

Cricket Futures – The lowdown on Somerset's changing climate

Mark Anderson

For millennia the Levels and Moors of Somerset were regarded as the 'Summer Lands'. However, it is only through drainage and artificial penning of water levels in recent centuries that has resulted in land mostly dry enough to be grazed the year round.

But it was not just the summer drying that gave this area its value as pasture, and latterly some arable. It was also its position in the rain-shadow area north east of Exmoor and the Quantocks. Indeed, the sunniness and relative dryness of the summer months continue to provide high quality grazing over most of the area between the Mendips and the Lias ridges that form the southern borders of this area.

For most of the last three millennia the combination of overall winter wetness contrasted with islands of summer pasture and sunniness nurtured an odd, almost unique, fauna. This was accentuated and influenced by the proximity of the sea. So, for example, we had here large numbers of the essentially coastal Great Green Bush Cricket, which also penetrated far inland, although only as far as the base of the hills marking the limits of the winter flooding. Nowadays, this species is much more restricted to the coast around Berrow dunes, though there are still island populations dotted around the edges of the levels and Moors, marking out what might be an ancient shore-line.

Suppose the climate of Britain were now to change markedly over the next two centuries or so. How would the change influence the species and quantities of the wildlife here? Will we see a resurgence of species such as the Great Green Bush Cricket? Will we see gains of species that have never been here? Can we already see the beginnings of change? And will there be a down-side to it all?

MA

THE GREAT GREEN BUSH CRICKET – A USEFUL INDICATOR OF CLIMATE CHANGE?

The dots show recorded locations of this animal in 2005, principally around the current and recent coastlines of our County. The animal is on the edge of its climatic range here – we should expect slight changes in climate to show themselves as restrictions of the insect's range to the current coast, or expansions over the whole of the Levels and Moors. No sign yet!

The line indicates boundaries of vice-counties 5 & 6.

The Orthoptera (grasshoppers and crickets) and their relatives, including such species as the Great Green Bush Cricket, are just the right ones to give early indications of climatic change. This is because most of the 50 or so species are pretty much on the northern or north-western edge of their distribution here, and because most can fly at least a few tens of metres. So we can watch for evidence of climatic change by seeing whether some of these species are expanding or contracting their ranges into or out of our area.

Of course, we cannot be certain that movements of distribution limits are due to climate change. They might result from other things happening at the same time, such as changes in agricultural practice or even changes in the road pattern (straw lorries coming from afar can bring living grasshoppers in their loads). Nonetheless, influxes and increases can be very suggestive and indicate that other similar faunistic changes may be on the way. They provide at least *circumstantial* evidence of climatic change, but only if they are of the sort that we know is likely from an understanding of species ecology. To extend this, we need also to understand what climatic changes are forecast and are actually occurring.

Britain sits in a climatic tension zone. We sit between the mass of Europe and the mass of the Atlantic. We are all familiar with the old idea that the North Atlantic Drift ('Gulf Stream') is nice warm water and gives us relatively warm air for our latitude, but in fact some other influences of our position are of direct importance too. Firstly, land warms up and cools down quicker than sea-water, and winds flow from a hot area to a cooler one, so we have very windy weather at times. There are a lot of these times because, secondly, our weather results from a train of cooling depressions running across the northern half of Britain. Sometimes the northern hemisphere's wavy ribbon of air at high altitude, called the 'Jet Stream', wiggles southwards a bit and drags the path of these depressions across the south of the country. This can have a sudden and marked effect – indeed most of the great lowland blizzards and storms of the last century resulted from depressions running up the English Channel next to Europe, or actually over the north of France. One way or another, this was the pattern of the hard winters of 1947, 1963 and 1978 (note the 15-year interval), and the great storms of 1987 and 1990. Nearly all of these had their influences on Somerset's Levels and Moors – pretty much in the front line of attack by western storms.

Now, the primary influence of increased heat energy in our global climatic belt must be an increase in the difference between land and sea temperatures, at least in extremes. So, whether or not we

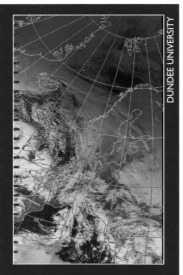

THE STORM OF 1990

A satellite image of the storm of January 30 1990, taken at 1230, just after its Somerset peak at mid-day. This small and intense depression has run up the English Channel and is centred over Somerset in the image. It is a type of damaging storm that may become more frequent here in the next few decades, influencing invertebrates through both wind-speed and temperature changes.

Mark Anderson

detect a change in mean temperatures, we can be certain of increased windiness, and probably of storminess too. We can go further than this, though, and suggest that we may have more southerly and south-easterly winds in storms. This is because a storm running up the English Channel has its top half over the south of Britain and this is where winds are predominantly from the east and south. No doubt, also, that if there is more energy in the system there will be higher land temperatures at maximum (though this might not be very appreciable) and this might just accentuate our summer sunniness here. And, if there is more energy available to evaporate water, there will be more rain, too.

So, we can forecast a gradual trend of increased windiness, storm frequency and raininess overall, with some rather less detectable increase in extreme high temperature and perhaps sunniness. How, precisely, might this affect grasshoppers and crickets? And have such effects yet been seen?

With one or two exceptions, our grasshoppers and crickets are very continental in their ecology. They are not very inconvenienced by harsh winters because they either spend this time as eggs buried in the ground and in dead vegetation, or as nymphs and adults buried in holes in the ground or deep in dead plant matter.

Oceanic summer weather, however, is a different kettle of fish as far as these creatures are concerned. Wet springs or summers promote fungal diseases and infestations. Even an averagely wet spring or summer, in combination with less-than-average temperatures can halve the size of any local population of our Orthoptera, and frequently does so. On the other hand increased warmth has a disproportionately beneficial influence on survival and breeding in most of our species. One degree up is worth a lot more than one degree down. As a first approximation, we might guess that the two minor effects of slightly raised temperature and sunniness will together just about balance that of expected increase in rainfall.

Overshadowing these effects to a large extent, however, is the major one of increased windiness and storminess. We can be pretty certain that we will not only see the effects of these over a period, but event by event as well. Indeed, the majority of changes that have so far been observed have been just the ones that would have been expected from the forecast change in winds. That is to say, we may have begun to see species expanding their distribution north-westwards into and across the Levels and Moors.

The vast majority of our native grasshoppers and crickets are winged. It is a curious thing that most of the ones that are not, or are almost not, are the most tolerant of oceanic conditions anyway, and have distributions already extending northwards at least to a line between Aberystwyth and Lowestoft. But a large number of the more fully winged and continental species barely reach our County, and yet it is these that we have begun to see coming in. The table below gives some idea of the pattern observed.

RECENT GAINS AND LOSSES OF ORTHOPTEROID SPECIES ON THE LEVELS AND MOORS		
	Consistent change with expected climate change	Non-consistent change with expected climate change
Species gained	4	1
Species lost	1	0

(Data based partly on observations of members of the Somerset Invertebrates Group and the Somerset Environmental Records Centre)

The two most impressive changes have been the influx of the Long-winged Conehead, and of Roesel's Bush-cricket. The conehead has long been in tall grassland along our southern coasts, but in just a decade has not only reached Somerset from the south-east but actually penetrated as far as the south-east corner of the Levels and Moors. We have no reason to think that this is due to changes in land-management alone, and so its influx is entirely likely to be a result of change in climate. Roesel's Bush-cricket, another tall-grass denizen, bears a slightly different tale - it seems to have reached here from the east in what might be a single 70km step. For a century or so it was known from the Thames estuary, then suddenly about twenty years ago it began to march westwards up the western streams of its main river. Suddenly we saw it beside the M5 at Bridgwater, nowhere near the Thames. This may well be the same trend as that responsible for the spread of the conehead, but it is also possible that the bush-cricket was brought on a motorway lorry. We will never know which. What is clear, though, is that both of these species came from the east and south-east, and both are now happily established here over quite large areas.

We have no example of an Orthopteran withdrawing to the south-east. The one loss (which may not be a loss at all, as the animal may well still exist on one part of the Moors), is the Large Marsh Grasshopper. The habitat here for some time has been atypical as its stronghold is on genuine quaking bogs, principally in Ireland. Ireland, you may know, is further west than Somerset. It will be

THE LONG-WINGED CONEHEAD –
VERY LIKELY TO BE EXPANDING IN RESPONSE TO CLIMATE

A decade ago this beast was only to be found on or near the south coast. Then it started to move north west (big arrow). About 1999 it reached the south-east corner of Somerset, and now is on to the Levels. The dot shows the most north-westerly point yet recorded for a probable migrant of this species, at Bishops Lydeard in August 2005.

interesting to see whether artificial re-wetting of parts of the Moors, combined with some tendency to increased ground wetness in spring and autumn, actually results in new records of this species. I would put the chances at 50:50, and this species must surely be a logical candidate for a local 'Recovery Programme', as long as site-management succeeds in generating new peat.

There is another wonderful but mysterious species that may come in the same category - the Mole Cricket. This must have been immensely widespread on peaty wet ground, and perhaps on some clay ground as underlies the Levels, too, until draining and ploughing got under way on an unforgiving scale a century or so ago. Indeed, there those who believe they have seen the animal once again recently on the very southern edge of the Levels and Moors. I have an email from a national specialist in such animals, saying that he thinks the record 'very likely'. Now, we may not need a local 'Recovery Programme' for this species as, notoriously, it comes in with foreign produce and garden materials. My guess is that the climate is at least as suitable for it as in the past and new trends towards sensitive management of wet grassland around here, themselves partly a response to anticipated climatic change, will result in it spreading. Since it flies quite well for 50 metres or so, I suggest you keep an eye out for this quite unmistakable hairy animal, with its lobster-like front legs. The time to look out for it is in May, after a storm, and you will most likely find it north-west of previous records. Quarter the ground between Creech St Michael and Bridgwater and I'll wager that you will see this beast on the move in the next ten years.

A most peculiar feature of Orthoptera is 'macroptery', the occasional development of unusually long wings. It is peculiar because it is not totally clear whether this is under environmental or genetic control. It is a sort of miniature version of that matter we all long ago learnt about locusts (which are, after all, just unreasonably big grasshoppers) - when the weather is right the next generation of locusts changes from ground-dwelling 'hoppers' to a flying form that devastates crops. In a similar way, most of our Orthoptera will suddenly sport long-winged forms. Authors of tomes on these animals are fond of using carefully-constructed sentences in their descriptions of this, implying that these long-winged or 'macropterous' animals do a lot more rushing about than the normal ones. This may be so, I don't know. Certainly, though, both Roesel's Bush-cricket and the Long-winged Conehead have been observed to have numbers of extra-long-winged animals in their new Somerset haunts. If, as is suggested for locusts, this change to long wings is at least partly under control by the weather, we have in these species rather good evidence that they will be able to conquer the long grass of the Levels and Moors within a decade if not within just a few years.

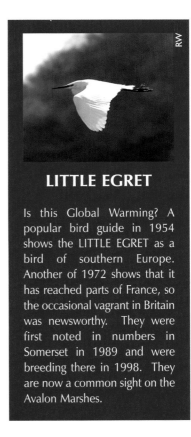

LITTLE EGRET

Is this Global Warming? A popular bird guide in 1954 shows the LITTLE EGRET as a bird of southern Europe. Another of 1972 shows that it has reached parts of France, so the occasional vagrant in Britain was newsworthy. They were first noted in numbers in Somerset in 1989 and were breeding there in 1998. They are now a common sight on the Avalon Marshes.

ROESEL'S BUSH CRICKET – AN UNEXPECTED NEW ARRIVAL FROM THE EAST

This animal began to travel westwards (big arrow) from the Thames estuary a couple of decades ago – one sort of pattern that might be expected from climate change. It reached the edge of the Levels at Bridgwater in about 2000, and has expanded to occupy an area of about 2 square kilometres. It may be expanding along the M5 corridor, too. The dot shows the point of arrival just south of Bridgwater.

We have seen some species, such as the Lesser Marsh Grasshopper, apparently expand in abundance or number of sites throughout Somerset in the last few years. However, I doubt that we can say at all that increases in number of sites, rather than distribution, are due to climate change, though they may be on the right scale and in the right places. This is because the species, such as the Lesser Marsh Grasshopper, that have leapt in apparent abundance recently, are more likely to have been badly identified, or just plain missed, in the past. There are a couple of orthopteroid species here, that may have increased recently, including the Woodland Grasshopper and Lesne's Earwig, that are certainly distinctive and unlikely to have been misidentified, but they are not particularly denizens of the Levels and Moors.

Are there other species, not previously native to the Levels and Moors, that might be expected soon? Indeed yes, and pretty excitingly so, too! Two of them are true crickets, and fine singers to boot. Indeed, the highly-musical Field Cricket is not far away – on the outskirts of Taunton – and there are rumours of such animals in Yeovil as well.

Now, our native Field Cricket was never officially recorded on the Levels and Moors , though I bet that it was around the edges of them a century and a half a go before the big 'plough-up' began. The Times of 19th August 2005 bears a half-page on the release of many Field Crickets in the south and east of England by the national 'Recovery Programme', perhaps the next batch of such animals might include some to be released on suitable ground in our County? Be that as it may, though, Field Crickets will be making their way, indeed they are doing so already, on to village land on and around the Levels and Moors. I emphasise that I am not referring to our native cricket, but the almost-identical Southern Field Cricket of Europe.

What is most significant, though, is that the Southern is the more likely to colonise our area, and for some very clear reasons. It breeds like a rabbit when conditions are right. Perhaps the native, or northern, species once did, but those involved in its 'Recovery Programme' have sent me an email saying that they have found it now to be a 'pig to breed', perhaps because it is down to a small genetic base as it only lived on one site in Sussex before the programme began. In contrast the breeding of the Southern species is so easy that pet-food suppliers throughout Britain sell it in boxes of 50 to be fed to captive lizards. It gets loose. We have begun to find it living outdoors for all or much of the year in some numbers just west of Taunton. There are hints, also, that it has begun to breed there.

DS

DS

Incoming Cricket (Field Crickets)

The Southern Field Cricket (top, with two yellow spots), and the Field Cricket (bottom, with broad yellow band). The incoming Southern is alive and well and living in places around the Levels and Moors. This one was photogaphed this year, 2005, just outside Taunton. The native, but virtually identical, Field Cricket is long-gone from Somerset, if indeed it ever lived here. The Southern species could be the more likely to establish itself here with climate change.

There is little doubt that people who live in villages have occasional pet lizards, too, and so crickets of this species are making their way into the countryside gradually as escapees from lizard-foodboxes. It is only very recently that these Southern Crickets have been able to survive in the wild, and this is quite possibly in part a response to climatic change. We can anticipate breeding colonies of several years duration dotted about. The presence of numbers of short-term colonies of this cricket would have one quite stunning effect on our countryside – it would bring back the long-lost sound of warm summer evenings. The two species of Field Cricket both have the same very loud chirruping and continuous song (made by rubbing the two forewings together) and this is well within the range of the human ear. It can be heard fifty or sometimes even a hundred metres from its source; it is as loud as birdsong.

A second cricket, not so loud but still attractively voiced, lives close to our southern borders and may be poised to enter the County. This is the Wood Cricket, which is present in parts of East Devon and the Taw valley of North Devon. Like the Field Cricket, it is extremely common just across the Channel in Normandy. It is not restricted to woods, as its name might suggest, but occurs virtually anywhere that has dead leaves for it to get beneath in winter. Hedgerows of all sorts support it and I have seen it in enormous numbers, alongside the Field Cricket, in the Cotentin Marshes of the Cherbourg peninsula, a landscape very similar indeed to our Levels and Moors. The Wood Cricket, like its Field relative, is not very mobile but it now builds up very large populations in its Devon haunts in most years. It is clear that our southern British climate is now mostly suitable for it. Occasionally, it is thought, nymphs or adults, perhaps eggs, of this species get transported incidentally from site to site in this country on the roots of transplanted trees or shrubs, maybe also on heathers, and so there is a means by which it will eventually come here. I am quite sure that it is able to spread through the hedgerows bounding fields on the Levels and on the edges of the Moors at about 25 metres a year. We should watch for it, and listen.

So, overall, we have some indications that grasshoppers, crickets and their relatives are moving in and that others may follow in conditions that are becoming predominantly more suitable climatically. We have few indications of actual or likely losses. The picture looks rosy. Is there a potential downside, a blot on the horizon? Actually there are two, but I have left them to the end because there is no evidence that they are going to be significant, and so I would not like to give them undue emphasis. I describe them briefly below, together with their possible consequences.

The first threat, familiar to watchers of television documentaries on our climate, is that the Atlantic Conveyor might stop. Indeed, a small number of authorities, and a much larger number of television

Opposite page: Increased rain and humidity? LN

producers, will tell you that it is already stopping. The consequences are always presented as dire. I doubt that they would be as dire for grasshoppers and their relatives here as the picture generally given suggests.

The Conveyor is the vertical, as well as the more familiar horizontal flow of the North Atlantic Drift that circulates water between low and high latitudes. Because of changes in seawater density depending on temperature and the input of freshwater to the North Atlantic, the down-flow of water around the Shetlands and east of Iceland can sometimes be stopped altogether. This can happen if, for example, increased energy in the atmosphere results in higher evaporation and hence rainfall rates in the north of Russia – more fresh water enters the North Atlantic and the Conveyor stops. One extreme forecast suggests that this could happen in 50 years; the loss of warmth coming into Britain from the North Atlantic drift would cool us all down in the winter and give us 1963-type snowfall one year in seven instead of one year in fifty.

This would be a change to a continental pattern, and most of our grasshoppers and crickets have a continental ecology. I suspect that even the extreme forecast above would only have gradual dele-terious effect on our species, which are mostly shut down and protected in dead plants during the winter. And, since we would not be protected from summer heating-up as happens further south in Europe, we might well have higher temperatures here in the summer balancing lower ones in the winter. Probably, also, we would have the increased windiness that results from being in between a

GR

A PEST TO AVOID, THE DEER TICK

The Deer Tick *Ixodes ricinus* is a parasite which attaches itself to the skin of mammals (including Man) and sucks their blood for food. This species is a hard-bodied tick which means its body does not swell up when it takes a meal and is therefore difficult to find until the bite starts itching. It is black and about the size of a pin head. To remove it, dab it with methylated spirits, alcohol, antiseptic or even smelly soap! This makes it relax its hold and it can be removed with forceps (or tweezers). If the bite area develops a circular rash around it, perhaps accompanied by 'flu'-like symptoms, visit your doctor. Deer Ticks carry the bacterial Lymes' disease which can have serious effects on joints, the heart and nervous system, but it can be treated with specific antibiotics. Numbers of these ticks have increased greatly over the last decade, probably due to warmer winters and the larger numbers of Roe Deer in Somerset, but you can avoid picking up the ticks by wearing socks over trouser ends and long sleeves.

Pat Hill-Cottingham

hot summer continent and a colder sea. These two things would counter any deleterious winter effects for Orthoptera generally in our area. I'm not suggesting that loss of the Conveyor would be beneficial, but I am suggesting that it would not be disastrous for our species. I also see no evidence that there will be a sudden turn-off in the climate due to loss of the conveyor.

The second, and even more minor, risk is the loss of the defence structures keeping the sea from the Levels, or the loss of pumping. Forecast increases of sea-level of up to 10m in the next century, and even of a large increase in the frequency of storms, are not going to overwhelm the structures that we have, and economically-valuable land-use of some sort is undoubtedly going to continue to be sufficiently important that water levels will continue on the same general pattern as we see now. Very likely we will see further purposeful wetting, partly to favour wildlife, and that wildlife will include Orthoptera. But since many of our characteristic Levels and Moors Orthoptera are essentially wetland or coastal species anyway, we should not expect to lose them.

This article has given an indication of the most likely change in climatic pattern over the next century or so. It is characterised more by an increase in storminess and wind than by increased temperature and sunniness, though these things will happen as well.

Grasshoppers and their relatives are likely to be good early indicators of such changes because many are biologically on their limits on our Levels and Moors – we can see the effects on them in the form of gross changes in distribution. Many other animals might show the same patterns in due course. We are now seeing Roesel's Bush-cricket and the Long-winged Conehead coming rapidly into this area from the east and south-east – this is the generally expected axis of gains and losses – and these changes are consistent with what we would expect from the forecast climatic changes. Some interesting species, particularly of true crickets, are poised to enter our borders, or already thrusting in, and we should look for them.

Latest Cricket update: On 21 August 2005, as I was taking a break from writing this article, I found a Long-winged Conehead in my garden at Bishops Lydeard 7 km north-west of Taunton. This is the first that I have heard of west of Taunton, and may indicate that these animals have now crossed from coast to coast – Bishops Lydeard is just 15 miles from the Bristol Channel. If so, the likelihood is that this species is now established on the Levels and Moors.

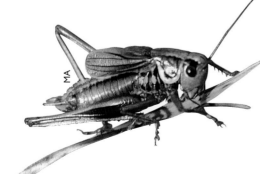

The Somerset Everglades –
A future vision for the Wetlands?

Andy King

What does the future hold for the Somerset Levels and Moors? With their unique comb-ination of landscape, wildlife, people and atmospheric 'sense of place', most people would readily agree that the Somerset wetlands are indeed a special place and unquestionably deserve a successful and thriving future. The previous sections in this book provide ample justification of the historical, cultural and environmental richness and importance which this area contains.

However, within the next few decades the Somerset Wetlands face tough challenges; difficult deci-sions which will set the future direction for the area and its inhabitants cannot be avoided or delayed much longer.

Although the exact effects and impacts of climate change on the Somerset Levels and Moors remain debatable, the fact that observable changes are happening right now around us is inescapable. Within the next eighty years or so, a sea level rise of 0.5 m in this area is predicted and generally accepted. However, recent measurements of the rate of ice retreat in the polar regions has further alarmed many scientists and in reality the figure of 0.5 m may turn out to be a considerable underestimate. A scenario of more extreme weather conditions with longer wetter winters, frequent flood events, and hotter drier summers is widely regarded as the inevitable shape 'of things to come'.

We are also seeing changes in agricultural practice; maintaining viability of dairy and cattle farming is becoming more difficult, there are the uncertainties over Common Agricultural Policy reform, there are pressures of cheaper imports from outside the area and an increasingly ageing population of farmers on the Somerset Levels and Moors. Financial support from new agri-environmental payment

ENGLISH NATURE

Flooded land (Candelabra).

BOTH PHOTOGRAPHS ENGLISH NATURE

Top left: Pelicans.

Top right: Water buffalo.

schemes, such as 'Entry Level' and 'Higher Level' schemes, is only designed to be available for the next 10 years or so. A controversial and emotive question looms about the future viability and sustainability of supporting existing farming practices in the Somerset wetlands with agricultural subsidies – is this approach really in the best longer term interests of the area itself, or the British tax-payer, or 'UK plc'?

A number of factors are absolutely crucial to ensure that we can successfully adapt to the forthcoming changes on the Somerset wetlands. We need to learn to live better with water, how to 'farm' water by acknowledging the role the land has as an asset in terms of storing and managing floodwater. We need to make proper, integrated use of the whole wetlands catchment, recognising how management of the upland areas can impact upon the lower floodplain – for example by the creation of habitats which slow the rate of run-off into the floodplain. We need to be more flexible and change our ways of thinking so we work *with* the forces of change rather than trying to resist them

THE TIDES OF CHANGE – REALIGNING THE COAST

The Steart Peninsula in Bridgwater Bay has flooded many times during the last millennium; in fact there have been several flood events in recent years, noticeably in1981, 1990 and 1997. Although the Steart coastal defences have been repaired and upgraded, a combination of wave action, coastal erosion and rising sea levels continues to weaken the existing defences; whilst the earth banks currently remain secure, the shingle ridge has become lower and narrower. Most of the land between Stolford and Combwich, to the rear of the existing sea defences, lies below the level of the highest yearly tide. In the event of a failure of the defences or an extreme flood, land and property would certainly be at considerable risk. Furthermore, with sea levels rising, and increased storminess predicted as a result of climate change, the situation is very likely become worse in the future, making the defences even more vulnerable.

However, the year-on-year maintenance and repair costs of the existing sea defences is not a cheap option. In any case, is the construction and upkeep of hard, engineered structures really a viable and sustainable solution to what will inevitably occur naturally? Is it really practical or sensible to literally try to keep the tides 'at bay'?

Fortunately, in this case, it is nature and the tides themselves that provide a possible answer to this dilemma – but it requires a radical, bold and somewhat ironic first step. One of the future management options being considered for the peninsula is to help protect the village of Steart by actually letting certain areas of land become flooded by the tide! The land given over to the effects of the tides could quickly develop into salt marsh and creeks; such environments are ideal at absorbing tidal wave energy and reducing the effects of coastal erosion. This 'managed realignment' option combined with the construction of smaller, sea defences built further inland could provide a cheap, cost-effective solution. It will also of course require careful consideration of how to maintain safe and reliable access for people in and out of Steart.

There are also environmental benefits in following a 'managed realignment' option at Steart. Salt-marsh environments and their associated reed-bed and coastal grazing-marsh habitats have been declining at an alarming rate from the English coastal landscape. The adoption of a 'managed realignment' scheme on the Steart Peninsula would not only help provide a sustainable and cheaper option to help safeguard the Steart and its community, but would also provide the opportunity to create a variety of brackish and salt marsh habitats of very high wildlife value.

The most difficult and challenging step in this process is actually the first one – letting nature and the tides take their course, and allowing the sea to encroach over land which has previously been defended.

Porlock, the breach in shingle bank allowed marine flooding to create new salt marsh.

Andy King

and engineer our way-out. The consequences of relying on a 'build the levees higher' approach are painfully inadequate as the recent disastrous floods in New Orleans have proved.

So, what could a future vision for the Somerset wetlands look like? Within a short to medium term, up to 2020, weather patterns are likely to shift towards more extreme and prolonged winter flood events and drier summers. These changes, in combination with higher tides will result in longer periods of tidal lock. Increased innundation of the wetlands will lead in some areas to habitats changing towards mosaics of swamps, wet fen, wet woodland and floodplain grasslands. Many of todays' farmers will have retired, and for those that remain, lower lying areas will become more inappropriate for some existing farming practices, especially certain grazing regimes.

Over a longer time period, 2050 and beyond, sea levels will continue to rise, and along the Somerset coast a possible consequence may be a decisive shift in policy to protect only major coastal settlements. This could result in lower-lying agricultural hinterland becoming subject to more frequent tidal flooding and the large-scale abandonment of current farming practices. The inability to remove water may result in some areas being wet for much of the year with grazing being carried out in an opportunistic basis and making use of other forms of cattle better suited to the conditions, such as water buffalo.

Inland, flood defence expenditure may become targeted to protect major towns such as Taunton and Bridgwater, and important communication links such as the M5 and main rail line (both of which in places may have to be raised or diverted to higher ground). An improved understanding and appreciation of natural wetland systems will be required to better predict flood events, but the harsh reality for some smaller settlements is that they may have to face the painful upheaval of being relocated.

Within the floodplain itself, traditional rural incomes which have been lost will need to be replaced by alternative wetland-derived incomes from harvesting reedbeds, aquaculture, fisheries, wildfowling, tourism and recreation. The upper parts of the catchment area will become more important for the sustainable production of food and crops formerly grown on the floodplain.

Increased flooding will result in further major habitat change and create extended wetland habitats including swamp, wet woodland and even 'everglade' type environments. Conservationists will have

Is the sun setting on existing farming... grazing regimes?

to accept the fact that protecting some of the special areas, formerly designated for particular wildlife or conservation reasons, is likely to become unsustainable – changes to habitats and water regimes will result in species migrating to other more suitable areas if these are available. Local extinctions of particular species are probably inevitable. However, in turn the 'new' environments will doubtless provide for a more diverse range of wetland habitats and species of equivalent, or even greater, ecological value.

The creation of reed swamps or 'everglade' type environments does *not* imply the creation of un-manageable areas of wilderness in which non-intervention is the norm. In fact, the opposite is true. Experience from the USA and elsewhere has amply demonstrated that maintaining an 'everglade' environment will require careful, sustained management if it is to be successful and viable for all its inhabitants, including us! The maintenance of diverse, ecological habitats alone will be challenging, but added to this will be the management requirements needed to unlock the enormous potential that such wetlands could have for local communities, employment and tourism.

Over the past few centuries generations of Somerset people have farmed the fields and managed the waterways on the Levels and Moors in such a way that they remain a unique and special place for us today. What could be more important than ensuring that we, as present day guardians of these wetlands, properly address the challenges that now face this area? We owe it to future generations to find a viable and sustainable future for the Somerset wetlands, so that they too can experience and enjoy their own 'special place' in the heart of Somerset.

A new addition to Somerset's biodiversity?

220

MY SOMERSET!

Misty mornings
Swallows fly low
Over the rhynes
And the withy row
The water glistens
A heron stands
Tall and majestic
In true command
As it takes to flight
The view we see
Is what the levels
Mean to me
Steeped in history
And to some degree
A product of man
Against the sea
The mighty, vast
King Sedgemoor Drain
The brackish reed swamps
Still remain
Dating back
To
Arthur's time
Where Norsemen roamed
And many a rhyme
Spoke of the great
And worshipped King
In Athelney
We think of him
A prince's island
In it's day
With marsh and reed
And sedge and clay
So take a moment
As the heron flies
To cast your eyes
Far and wide
Brent Knoll ahead
And then the Tor
With Burrow Mump
And in the fore
The barn owls, swans
Other wildfowl too
The Somerset Levels
From me to you

Jacqueline Briggs

Biographies of Contributors (in book sequence)

Bernard Storer After war service Bernard Storer gained a Natural Sciences degree at Cambridge and was much influenced by the ecology lectures of the late Professor H Godwin. Subsequently he obtained his teacher qualifications. After teaching in Derbyshire and Shropshire, in 1957 he joined the staff of Dr Morgan's School in Bridgwater. Settling in Westonzoyland he soon became fascinated by the ecology of the Levels and Moors. He wrote many articles, was involved in TV programmes, gave talks and escorted trips around the area he found so interesting. His ideas about the area are summed up in his book 'The Natural History of the Somerset Levels'. He was also much involved with the Somerset Wildlife Trust and the creation of their reserves at Catcott and Westhay. Though less active he still 'potters around' his much loved area.

WETLAND THROUGH TIME

Derek Briggs had a childhood interest in the creation of landscapes - real and imagined! He became a field geologist with the National Coal Board and subsequently entered the educational world, teaching geology and geography across the age range. Headship of an outdoor education centre followed and, with an extra qualification in Field Biology, he later held an advisory post for the Environmental Education in Somerset. Although officially retired, Derek's enthusiasm for an integrated approach to landscape studies still keeps him busy with consultancy and voluntary work. He is a past President of the Somerset Archaeological and Natural History Society and Secretary of its Natural History Committee.

Dr Andy King has been a keen enthusiast of Somerset geology since he first collected fossils from Kilve beach some 30 years ago. He studied at Richard Huish College, Taunton before graduating with an Honours Degree in Geology from Swansea University in 1986; he obtained his PhD in 1990 whilst working as an Arctic Geologist based in Cambridge. Employment with English Nature brought him back to Somerset where he worked as Conservation Officer for the Somerset Levels and Moors. He is currently English Nature's Area Manager for Somerset and Gloucestershire but still finds time to escape from behind his desk to enjoy the county he regards as 'home'.

Dennis Parsons is Curator of Natural Sciences at the Somerset County Museum: responsible for the management and development of an extensive collection of 250 000 biological and geological specimens from Somerset and beyond. Work interests lie in natural history and geology, especially palaeoecology, taphonomy and the reconstruction of ancient sedimentary environments.

Vanessa Straker is an environmental archaeologist specializing in archaeobotany. Since moving to the south west in 1983, she has been involved with many projects in the Levels and Moors. She has been English Heritage South West Region's Advisor for Archaeological Science since 1999 and is also concerned with English Heritage's strategy for Wetland Archaeology

Richard Brunning first worked on the Somerset wetlands as part of an archaeology degree and subsequent wetland course at Exeter University. After many years of working on wetland archaeological sites in Scotland, Wales and Ireland he became the Levels and Moors Archaeologist for Somerset County Council in 1993, a post he still holds.

Dr Stephen Rippon has carried out extensive research on the wetland landscapes of Somerset and more widely around the Severn Estuary, and has published The Gwent Levels: The Evolution of a Wetland Landscape (1996) and The Severn Estuary: Landscape Evolution and Wetland Reclamation (1997). He is reader in landscape archaeology at the University of Exeter.

Dr Robert Dunning was editor of the Victoria History of Somerset from 1967 until his retirement in 2005 but continues to be team leader of the Lottery-funded Southern Exmoor Settlement project. He is a graduate of Bristol University, a Fellow of the Society of Antiquaries of London and of the Royal Historical Society, and is a former Chairman and President of the Somerset Archaeological and Natural History Society.

Francis Farr-Cox has lived all his life on the coastal Levels. As well as acting as the county recorder for arachnids, giving talks and running workshops, he has a keen interest in the history of the Levels and Moors.

Roger Rogers was born and brought up near Glastonbury and followed his father in working peat on the Somerset Levels and Moors. In more recent years he has spent time teaching children, and other visitors to the Peat Moors Centre at Westhay, the traditional methods of peat extraction, passing on his knowledge and skills.

Jean Pilgrim is a Somerset native, with a background in farming and education. She has a life-long interest in the varied landscapes and history of Somerset. Growing up on a farm, she was fascinated, as a child, with the low, flat landscapes surrounding her. Later on, after bringing up her own children to enjoy their farm, she worked as a teacher in the County. She has helped lead a range of courses for teachers using, and introducing them to, the richness of the hills and wetlands. She focuses her work on 'Man and the Landscape' – exploring the geological, archaeological and historic aspects that the County has to offer.

Graham Rix a retired Head of Biology, Norton Hill School; the Manager for Somerset Wildlife Trust of Sharpham Moor Plot and Street Heath reserves; Chairman of the Peat Moors Advisory Group and served on SWT Council for many years. He is a member of Somerset Archaeological and Natural History Society and of its Natural History Committee and Secretary of the Somerset Invertebrates Group. His main interest, apart from ecology, is the photography of plants and invertebrates.

Eddie Wills began collecting woodlice in match boxes at the age of two and moved on to flint implements by the age of five. His interest in wildlife led him to a career in conservation, but Eddie's passion for Iron Age culture grew out of a college placement at a Cambridgeshire hillfort, to cover all aspects of the Celtic way of life from Prehistoric farming practices and craft skills to mythology and beliefs. He has over twenty years experience as an environmental educator and never tires of sharing his enthusiasm with young people.

WETLAND AND WILDLIFE

Dr Martin Drake is a freelance entomologist specialising in conservation issues. Previously, he worked as an entomological specialist for the Nature Conservancy Council and English Nature. He has a particular interest in the fauna of grazing marshes and has surveyed a large number of sites in many counties over the past 20 years.

Sarah Cross has a BSc (Hons) degree in Environmental Science. After graduating she worked for the Countryside Council for Wales covering the Gwent Levels and since 2002 has been a Conservation Officer with English Nature on the Somerset Levels.

Phil Holms Though somewhat of a newcomer to Somerset, Phil Holms brings more than 30 years of conservation management expertise to his present Somerset Levels role, of English Nature Site Manager for Shapwick Heath National Nature Reserve, near Glastonbury. Driven by a keen interest in nature since early childhood, Phil has previously worked for The Nature Conservancy and later The Nature Conservancy Council, on a variety of wetland sites in England.

Olivia Keith was Artist in Residence at the Peat Moors Centre between April and October 2005. She worked on projects with children, mothers and toddlers and disabled groups. Apart from the Shapwick Giant project, she left behind the timber slab Story Bench decorated with children's art work which can be seen on Shapwick Nature Reserve.

David Riley lives on the Polden Hills on a 10 acre smallholding which is also a county wildlife site recording such unusual species as Nightjar and Barn Owl, the latter being encouraged back to breed for three successive years. The site has recently been opened to create glades in an attempt to encourage the Nightingales back to the area. There are some 10 notable or rare wildflowers on the south facing calcareous grassland escarpment. David regularly broadcasts on BBC Somerset Sound with a monthly synopsis on events in the Somerset countryside. He also writes a monthly article for the local publication 'Polden Post'. He has recently been awarded a Green Apple in recognition of his work on the county wildlife site. In recent times he was given a Millennium Award to design and write a broadsheet on the wildlife in Sedgemoor distributed to Sedgemoor residents and schools.

Lynne Newton was born in rural Lancashire where she inherited her love of wildlife and the countryside. She moved to Somerset two years ago after working for the Metropolitan Police in the Wildlife Crime Unit at Scotland Yard. This gave her more time to follow her hobbies and her photography has developed into a consuming passion. Much of her time is spent on the Levels chasing the moods of weather, sunrise and dusk and anything that moves!

Dr Stephanie Greshon runs her own Ecological Consultancy business based near Frome, in Somerset. Most of her work comprises Ecological Impact Assessments but she specialises in botanical survey techniques. Training new ecologists entering the profession is also an important part of her work and she has been running ecological CPD courses for Bristol University for 10 years.

Katherine Emms is a recent graduate from Cardiff University where she gained a First Class Honours Degree in Biology. While at Cardiff she did her research project on Tropical Marine Ecology, involving a field trip to Tobago. She has since completed a PGCE and will be starting her first teaching job at Frome Community College in September.

Dr Pat Hill-Cottingham graduated in Honours Zoology at King's College, London, where she also gained her PGCE. Later she gained a further qualification in teaching Field Biology and recently completed her PhD with the Open University. She manages Catcott North Reserve for Somerset Wildlife Trust, is a member of its Peat Moors Advisory Committee and is especially interested in the ecology and conservation of late succession molluscs and ferns. She was a founder member of the Somerset Invertebrates Group and is its Education Secretary. She is Chairman of Somerset Archaeological and Natural History Society, Chairman of its Natural History Committee, and a past president.

David Boyce is an ecological consultant specialising in invertebrate ecology and conservation with a particular interest in the British beetles.

Dr Philip Radford, a retired general practitioner, has a long interest in natural history. Birds are his main interest, especially their behaviour; emphatically, he is no 'twitcher'! He has always admired dragonflies, particularly their colourful patterns, and enjoys attempting to photograph them. Wildlife sound is another interest and he contributes recordings to the National Sound Archive, Wildlife Section, of the British Library. He lives on the Quantock Hills and likes to walk in the local woods but, as a change, a visit to the wetlands of the Somerset Levels is always enjoyed. He has been Chairman and President of Somerset Archaeological and Natural History Society and is a member of its Natural History Committee.

Keith Gould was born in Taunton in 1950, and educated at North Town Junior School before moving on to Taunton School. Here he was inspired into a lifelong interest in Wildlife and Natural History by his teacher the late Dr. Ernest Neal. On leaving school he was employed by Musgrove Hospital and was sent to Bristol College where he attained qualifications in Histology and Cytology. A change in direction leads to other qualifications in Timber Technology and he is now self-employed as a furniture maker. A Committee member of the local branch of Butterfly Conservation he now gives talks all over the county on Somerset Butterflies and some of the more exotic foreign species taken on his travels worldwide with his wife Eileen. When time permits he helps with the management of Thurlbear Quarrylands Reserve.

Sally Mills has worked with the RSPB for the last 16 years, which has enabled her, not only to pursue a career she believes in, but also to fulfill a desire to work with the natural environment. This career has led her to interesting places around the country, working on a variety of nature reserves, each with its own challenges. However, her work on the Avalon Marshes in Somerset over the last ten years has been the biggest and most exciting challenge yet – the transformation of a peat-extracted landscape into a mosaic of wetland habitats. This is a unique opportunity to turn the clock back for nature on a significant scale.

David Chown has a keen interest in wildlife, especially birds, since childhood. His first job in conservation (habitat surveying for English Nature in Somerset) arrived courtesy of the Community Programme in 1982, and he has been involved in bird survey and research since then, initially mainly for the RSPB. In 1997 he became a self-employed consultant. Most of his work has been in the south-west, on the Levels, uplands and coast.

Tony Serjeant is Somerset County Council's Ecologist with special responsibility for advising the authority on the impacts of the peat industry on the Levels and Moors. He has a BSc degree in Zoology from Durham University and MScs in Conservation Biology and Environmental Rehabilitation obtained respectively from the Universities of Kent and Aberystwyth. He is a founder member of the Somerset Invertebrates Group and his interest in wet woodlands stems from the value of this habitat for a range of rare and unusual invertebrate animals. He is a member of Somerset Archaeological and Natural History Society Natural History Committee

Russell Gomm is a retired naturalist who has lived for the past 30 years alongside the River Tone near the edge of the Somerset Moors. Having spent all his working life in the field of natural history and wildlife conservation (with English Nature), he has, since retirement, taken a particular interest in the wildlife associated with the R Tone in the vicinity of Creech St Michael, producing a report on the wildlife of the Parish at the turn of the century. He has, for many years, been a member of the Somerset Otter Group, which monitors the activity of these animals throughout the County. He was, until recently, a member of Council and the Natural History Committee of Somerset Archaeological and Natural History Society but has now moved out of Somerset.

WETLAND – WHAT FUTURE?

Dr Peter Beeden has been in agriculture all his working life. After a pre-college year farm labouring, he worked in agricultural research and development in Malawi and Nigeria, before dairy farming in South Wales, moving later to beef and sheep. By 1982, farming was complemented with numerous short-term missions to Africa, Asia and Middle East to prepare, supervise, technically support and evaluate development projects to raise the food and cash crop production of subsistence farmers. In 1997 he joined Somerset Wildlife Trust's Wildlife Sites Project to support managers of important wildlife habitats. Barbara and Peter still run their farm business and continue some overseas work.

Dr Mark Anderson is a botanist who has spent most of his career as a mathematical ecologist, starting off by doing a PhD in Wales on population dynamics of sedges in dune slacks (an esoteric subject if ever there was one!). He went on to lead ecological research for the Forestry Commission in the impact of exotic trees and harvesting on plant populations and soils, in meteorology and phenology, and developed new conservation practices. After this he ran a number of consultancies, including work in Brazil and the Serengeti, and in Britain on the Chernobyl fallout. From 1989 to 1992 he was the first Director of the Somerset Environmental Records Centre, starting off its current role as a consulting firm. Since then he has concentrated on expert child-minding, with additional work supervising PhD students for the OU. He was a founder of many of the Specialist Groups of Somerset and is currently the Orthoptera Taxon Coordinator for the Somerset Invertebrates Group. His underlying interests are in the rational use of land, man-management and the crucial role of the amateur in applied science. He is now working on practical means of applying the mathematics of chaos to wildlife conservation on a landscape scale.

Jacqueline Briggs was born in Somerset's County town, Taunton, and brought up in the local villages of Nether Stowey and Combwich. She has always enjoyed the wildlife and changing seasons of the Somerset Levels, from cycling as a child to driving to work and walking as an adult. The misty mornings have always been a favourite. Now happily married and living in a 15th century farmhouse on the Poldens, she is learning more of the history and legends of her home county, as well as continuing to enjoy its beauty and wildlife.

Higher Ropes Drove.

Glossary

alluvium: sediment transported and deposited by flowing estuarine or river water

artefact: a product of human art and workmanship

Blue Lias: a part of the Lower Jurassic rock sequence; from a quarryman's dialect term for rocks showing clear layers ('lias') of a blue-grey colour

bog: an acid mire area fed by rain and poor in mineral salts

carr: a late stage in plant succession, shrub and woodland (mainly willow and alder)

Chaser, Darter, Hawker, Skimmer: types of dragonfly based on the shape of the body, especially the relative length of the abdomen

coastal realignment: allowing encroachment of the sea and the development of salt marsh as an alternative to maintaining sea defences

community: all the living organisms in a habitat

Crustacea: invertebrate animals with an exoskeleton and seven pairs of legs, including water louse and freshwater shrimp

dendrochronology: dating by means of tree rings (the growth rings seen in a cross-section of a trunk)

diatoms: microscopic single-celled algae with a wall impregnated with silica

drove: a track way allowing movement of farm machinery and people between fields on the Somerset Levels and Moors

eutrophic: water high in salts and organic matter, and low in oxygen, due to the decay of vegetable matter by bacteria

fault: a fracture in rock which shows displacement of the opposite sides

fauna: animals

fen: a mire rich in calcareous salts e.g. calcium

flagstone: a sandstone which splits easily and relatively thinly

flood plain: a flat area of land bordering a river and periodically inundated by flood water

flora: plants

Foraminifera: microscopic single-celled animals with a shell of calcium carbonate

global warming: increasing temperatures of the planet as a result of higher levels of greenhouse gases such as carbon dioxide and methane

herb: a green plant which does not undergo secondary thickening (i.e. no wood formation as in a shrub or tree)

insect development: direct – egg to larva (caterpillar) to pupa (chrysalis) to inago (adult); indirect – egg to a series of nymphal instars to adult; the final change into the adult form is known as metamorphosis

inundation: submersion of land under water, including flooding

Levels: coastal and river-mouth low-lying flatlands of Somerset where the peat is covered with clay

mesotrophic: a very general term introduced to cover the nutritive salt levels in water or on land which are between the low (oligotrophic) and excessive (eutrophic)

mire: a general term for a wet area of vegetation

Mollusca: invertebrates including snails and slugs, octopus, squid, Nautilus and fossil ammonites; spirally coiled shells are gastropods, shells with two hinged parts are called bivalves

Moors: inland low-lying flatlands of Somerset where peat is at the surface

oxidation: addition of oxygen to or removal of hydrogen from a compound

pollen analysis: determination of past existence of plants by identification of pollen surviving in soil samples

raised bog: an actively growing peat-forming system of tussocks and hummocks of Sphagnum (moss) surrounded by wet areas

Ramsar site: a term covering globally important wetland sites, categorised at a meeting held in the town of Ramsar in Czechoslovakia

ribs (of ammonites): corrugations across the whorls of the shell

rhyne: a waterway under control of a Local Drainage Board; usually larger than a ditch (field boundaries controlled by the landowner) but smaller than a drain (large drainage channel under control of the Environment Agency)

silt: particles of sediment intermediate in size between fine sand and clay grains (1/16 mm – 1/256 mm or 62.5μm - 4μm)

stratum, (pl. strata): layer – usually referring to layers within a succession of rocks or soil

succession: the floral and faunal changes occurring in a habitat with time

taxon, (pl. taxa): any group in the classification of plants and animals, from kingdom to species

thrust: a fracture in rock caused by compression so that one side is pushed over the other at a low angle

Vice-county: a system introduced in 1852 by H.C. Watson of similar-sized areas convenient for recording

withy: the name given to stems of willow, in particular *Salix viminalis* or Osier

zone: (geology) a group of rock strata characterised by a closely defined fossil content, or (natural history) an area characterised by a typical suite of plant and/or animal species

Acronyms Used in the Text

AONB	Area of Outstanding Natural Beauty
BAP	Biodiversity Action Plan
BSBI	Botanical Society of the British Isles
DEFRA	Department of the Environment and Rural Affairs
EA	Environment Agency
EN	English Nature (formerly Nature Conservancy Council, to become Natural England in October 2006)
ESA	Environmentally Sensitive Area/Environmental Stewardship Area
HAP	Habitat Action Plan
IACS	Integrated Administration and Control System
NNR	National Nature Reserve
Ramsar	Internationally important wetland site
RDB	Regional Drainage Board
RSPB	Royal Society for the Protection of Birds
RWLA	Raised Water Level Area
SAC	Special Area of Conservation
SANHS	Somerset Archaeological and Natural History Society
SAP	Species Action Plan
SCC	Somerset County Council
SERC	Somerset Environmental Records Centre
sp.	species (plural spp.)
SPA	Special Protection Area
SSSI	Site of Special Scientific Interest
SWT	Somerset Wildlife Trust (formerly STNC Somerset Trust for Nature Conservation)
WeBS	Wetland Bird Survey
WT	Wildlife Trusts (formerly RSNC Royal Society for Nature Conservation)

Archaeology and History: References and Bibliography

Adby R Brunning R A & Webster C J 2001. The discovery of a Roman villa at Shapwick and its Severan coin hoard of 9238 silver denarii. *Journal of Roman Archaeology*, 14, 358-372

Alderton A M 1983. The Sedgemoor Survey 1982: Environmental Results. *Somerset Levels Papers* 9, p9-18

Allen J R L & Rae J E 1987. Late Flandrian shoreline oscillations in the Severn Estuary: a geomorphological and stratigraphic reconnaissance. *Philosophical Transactions of the Royal Society* B315, 185-230.

Allen J R L 2001. Sea level, salt marsh and fen: Shaping the Severn Estuary Levels in the later Quaternary (Ipswichian-Holocene). *Archaeology in the Severn Estuary*, 11, 13-34

Ashworth N 2004. *Voices from the Peat, An Oral History of the Avalon Marshes.* SCC

Aston M & Burrow I 1982. *The Archaeology of Somerset.* Somerset County Council

Brunning R, Jones J & West S 1995. Excavations at Benedict Street, Glastonbury, 1993: a study in environmental change from the Neolithic to the Iron Age. Proceedings of the *Somerset Archaeological and Natural History Society*, 139, 17-45

Brunning R 2005. Unique, unrivalled and disappearing, what hope for Somerset's wetland heritage? *Proc. SANHS* Vol 146 165-169

Bulleid A & Gray H St G 1911. *The Glastonbury Lake Village Volume 1.* Glastonbury

Bulleid A & Gray H St G 1917. *The Glastonbury Lake Village Volume 2.* Glastonbury

Bulleid A & Gray H St G 1948. *The Meare Lake Village Volume 1.* Glastonbury

Caseldine A E 1988. A wetland resource: the evidence for the environmental exploitation of the Somerset Levels during the prehistoric period. In Murphy P, and French C (eds) *The exploitation of wetlands.* British Archaeological Reports, British Series, 186, 239-265

Clapham A R & Godwin H 1948. Studies in the post-glacial history of British vegetation: VIII Swamping surfaces in the Somerset levels: IX Prehistoric trackways in the Somerset Levels. *Philosophical Transactions of the Royal Society* 13, 233-73

Coles J M & Coles B J 1986. Sweet Track to Glastonbury

Coles J M & Coles B J 1989. Prehistory of the Somerset Levels. Somerset Levels Project. Austin & Sons, Hertford

Coles J M, Goodall A & Minnitt S 1992. Arthur Bulleid and the Glastonbury Lake Village 1892-1992

Coles J M, Hibbert F A & Orme B J 1973 Prehistoric roads and tracks in Somerset: 3. The Sweet Track. *Proceedings of the Prehistoric Society* 39, 256-293

Druce D 1999. Late Mesolithic to early Neolithic environmental change in the central Somerset Levels: recent work at Burnham-on-sea. *Archaeology in the Severn Estuary, 9,* (for 1998), 17-29.

Dunning R W (ed) 2004. *A History of the County of Somerset Volume VIII The Poldens and the Levels.* Boydell & Brewer

Farr-Cox F 2005. The irrigation of the Somerset Levels. Proc. SANHS Vol 146, 170-172

Godwin Sir H 1960. Prehistoric wooden trackways of the Somerset Levels: their construction, age and relation to climate change. *Proc. Prehistoric Soc.* 26, 1-36

Godwin Sir H 1981. *The archives of the peat bogs.* Cambridge Univ Press. Cambridge

Gray H S G & Bulleid A 1953. *The Meare Lake Village Volume 2.* Glastonbury

Gray H St G 1966. *The Meare Lake Village Volume 3.* Glastonbury

Grove J & Brunning R 1999. The Romano-British salt industry in Somerset. *Archaeology in the Severn Estuary* 9, 61-68. Exeter. SELRC

Hancock C 2005. What future for the Somerset levels and Moors? *Proc. SANHS* Vol 146, 191-194

Haslett S K, Davies P, Davies, C F C, Margetts A J, Scotney K H, Thorpe D J & Williams H O 2001. The changing estuarine environment in relation to Holocene sea level and the archaeological implications. *Archaeology in the Severn Estuary*, 11, 35-53.

Heyworth A & Kidson C 1982. Sea-level changes in south west England and Wales. *Proceedings of the Geologists' Association,* 93(1), 91-111.

Housley R A, Straker V & Cope D W 2000. The Holocene peat and alluvial stratigraphy of the Upper Brue Valley in the Somerset Levels based on soil survey data of the 1980's. *Archaeology in the Severn Estuary 1999,* 10, 11-23

Jones J 1999. Plant macrofossil remains from Greylake, Somerset. *Unpublished report for Somerset County Council*

Jones J 2004. *Summary of palaeoenvironmental analyses carried out at Walpole Landfill Site, Pawlett Level, Somerset.* University of Bristol, unpublished report

Kidson C, Gilberston D D, Haynes J R, Heyworth A, Hughes C E & Whatley R C 1978. Interglacial marine deposits of the Somerset Levels south-west England. *Boreas* 7, 215-28

Leech R, Bell M & Evans J 1983. The sectioning of a Romano-British mound at east Huntspill. *Somerset Levels Papers* 9, 74-78

Masser P, Jones J, & McGill B, in press. Romano-British settlement and land-use on the Avonmouth Levels: the evidence of the Pucklechurch to Seabank pipeline project. *Trans Bristol and Gloucester Arch. Soc.*

Meddens F M & Bealsey M 2001. Roman seasonal wet pasture exploitation near Nash, on the Caldicot Levels, Wales, *Britannia* XXXII, 141-84

Minnitt S & Coles J M 1996. *The Lake Villages of Somerset* Taunton

Minnitt S 2001. *The Shapwick Treasure* Taunton

Quekett W 1888. My Sayings and Doings. 27-28

Rippon S 1994. Medieval Wetland Reclamation in Somerset, in M. Aston and C. Lewis eds. *The Medieval Landscape of Wessex,* 239-53. Oxford: Oxbow

Rippon S 1997. *The Severn Estuary: landscape evolution and wetland reclamation.* Leicester University Press

Rippon S 1995. Roman Settlement and Salt Production on the Somerset Coast: The Work of Sam Nash - A Somerset Archaeologist and Historian 1913-1985, *Proc. Somerset Arch.& Nat. Hist Soc.* 139, 99-117

Rippon S 1996. *Gwent Levels: The Evolution of a Wetland Landscape.* York: Council for British Archaeology Research Report 105

Rippon S 1997. *The Severn Estuary: Landscape Evolution and Wetland Reclamation.* London: Leicester University Press

Rippon S 2000a. The Romano-British Exploitation of Coastal Wetlands: Survey and Excavation on the North Somerset Levels, 1993-7, *Britannia* 31, 69-200

Rippon S 2000b. *The Transformation of Coastal Wetlands: Exploitation and Management of Marshland Landscapes in North West Europe during the Roman and Medieval Periods.* London: British Academy

Rippon S, Jackson A & Martin M 2001. The use of soil analysis in the interpretation of an early historic landscape at Puxton in Somerset, *Landscape History* 23, 27-38

Rippon S 2001. *Estuarine Archaeology: The Severn and Beyond.* Exeter: Severn Estuary Levels Research Committee

Rippon S 2002a. Infield and Outfield: the early stages of marshland colonisation and the evolution of medieval field systems. In Lane, T. (ed.) *Through Wet and Dry: essays in honour of David Hall,* 54-70. Sleaford: Heritage Lincolnshire

Rippon S 2002b. Adaptation to a changing environment: the response of marshland communities to the late medieval 'crisis'. *Journal of Wetland Archaeology* 1, 15-39

Rippon S 2004a. *Historic Landscape Analysis.* York: CBA Handbook

Rippon S 2004b. A Push into The Margins? The development of a coastal landscape in North West Somerset (UK) during the late 1st millennium AD. In J. Hines, A. Lane and M. Redknap (eds) *Land, Sea, and Home: Proceedings of a Conference on Viking-period Settlement (Cardiff, July2001),* 359-78

Rippon S 2004c. Making the most of a bad situation? Glastonbury Abbey and the exploitation of wetland resources in the Somerset Levels. *Medieval Archaeology* 48, 91-130

Rippon S 2005. Taming a wetland wilderness: Romano-British and Medieval reclamation in the Somerset Levels and Moors. *Proc. SANHS* Vol 146 157-164

Rippon S (forthcoming). *Landscape and Community: landscape evolution on the North Somerset Levels* York: CBA Research Report

Robinson M 2002. English Heritage Reviews of Environmental Archaeology: Southern Region Insects. Centre for Archaeology Report 39/2002

Somerset Levels Papers 1975-1989, 1-15

Stradling W 1849. The turbaries between Glaston and the Sea. *Proc. Som. Arch.& Nat. Hist. Soc.* 1, pt ii, 48-62

Straker V, Brunning R & Jones J 2002. The Brue Valley, Somerset: Holocene stratigraphy and palaeoecology and the possible influences of sea level change. Bath Spa University College Occasional Papers in geography (2002), 2, pp.31-36, ISSN 1472-8974

Tinsley H M 2003. *Pollen analysis of samples from peat and alluvium associated with a saltern near Woolavington Bridge, Huntspill River, Somerset.* University of Bristol, unpublished report

Wilkinson K 1999. An investigation of Holocene peat and intertidal stratigraphy on Shapwick Heath, Somerset: preliminary results. *Archaeology in the Severn Estuary*, **9,** (for 1998), 87-90

Williams M 1974. *The Draining of the Somerset Levels.* Cambridge

Geology: References and Bibliography

Croft R & Aston M 1993. *Somerset from the air.* Taunton

Duff K L, McKirdy A P & Harley M J (Eds.) 1985. *New sites for old – a student's guide to the geology of the east Mendips.* Nature Conservancy Council, 189pp.

Edmonds E A & Williams B J 1985. Geology of the country around Taunton and the Quantock Hills. *Memoir of the British Geological Survey, Sheet 295 (New Series).* HMSO. 92pp.

Farrer J S & Murless B J April 1997. Dunball Salt Works, *Somerset Industrial Archaeological Society Bulletin No. 74*

Hardy P 1999. *The Geology of Somerset.* Ex Libris Press. 224pp.
Howe S R, Sharpe T & Torrens H S 1981. *Ichthyosaurs: a history of fossil 'sea-dragons'.* National Museum of Wales, 31pp.
Hunt C O & Haslett S K (eds) 2006. *The Quarternary of Somerset: field guide.* Quarternery Research Association, Cambridge.

King A 1997. *Fossil Ammonites from the Somerset Coast.* Somerset County Museum Service & English Nature Publication, Short Run Press, Exeter. 18pp.

Lehmann U 1981. *The ammonites, their life and world.* Cambridge University Press. 246pp.

Mayr H 1992. *Collins Photo Guide to Fossils.* Harper Collins publishers, London. 256pp.
McGowan C 1992. *Dinosaurs, Spitfires and Sea Dragons.* Harvard University Press, 365pp.
Monks N & Palmer P 2002. *Ammonites.* Natural History Museum, London 159pp.

Taylor M A & Martin J G 1990. *Big mouths and Long necks.* Leicestershire Museums, Arts and Records Service, Publication No.110, 24pp.

Walker C & Ward D 1992. *Fossils - Eyewitness Handbook.* Dorling Kindersley, London. 320pp.
Whittaker A & Green G W 1983. Geology of the country around Weston-super-Mare. *Memoir of the Geological Survey of Great Britain, Sheet 279, with parts of sheets 263 and 295 (New Series).* HMSO. 148pp.

Natural History: References and Bibliography

Arnold E N & Burton J A 1978. *A Field Guide to the Reptiles and Amphibians of Britain and Europe.* Collins
Ashworth N 2004. *Voices from the Peat, an Oral History of the Avalon Marshes.* Somerset County Council

Ballance D K 2004. *A Bibliography of Somerset Ornithology.* Privately printed
Ballance D K to be published 2006. *The Birds of Somerset.* Isabelline Books
Blamey M, Fitter R & Fitter A 2003. *Wild Flowers of Britain & Ireland.* Black
Boyce D 2004 Ecology and conservation of the Lesser Silver Water Beetle *Hydrochara caraboides* on the Somerset Levels. *Proc SANHS* Vol 146, 183-185
Bratton J H, ed. (1992) *British Red data Books: 3. Invertebrates other than Insects.* Joint Nature Conservation Committee.
Brooks S 1997. *Field Guide to the Dragonflies and Damselflies of Great Britain and Ireland.* British Wildlife Publishing

Cameron R 2003. *Land Snails in the British Isles.* AIDGAP Field Studies Council
Chapman C (1996) *Secrets of the Levels.* Somerset Books
Chinery M 1989. *Butterflies and Day-flying Moths of Britain and Europe.* Collins
Chinery M 1986 *Collins Guide to the Insects of Britain & Western Europe.* Collins
Chinery M 1977 *The Family Naturalist.* Macdonald & Jane's
Chown D 1996 & 2002. *Breeding Birds of the Avalon Marshes.*
Chown D J 2001. *Nocturnal use of the Somerset Levels and Moors floodplain by overwintering waterfowl 2000/2001. A report to English Nature Somerset Team.*
Chown D J 2003. Night-time use of the Somerset Levels and Moors floodplain by waterfowl: final report, winters 2001/2002 and 2002/03. *A report to English Nature Somerset Team*
Clegg J 1966. *Pond Life* the Observers Series, Claremont Books
Corbet G B & Southern H N 1964. *The Handbook of British Mammals.* Blackwell
Courtecuisse R 1999. *Collins Wildlife Trust Guide to Mushrooms.* Collins
Croft P S 1986. *A Key to the Major Groups of Freshwater Invertebrates.* AIDGAP Field Studies Council

Davis S & Jarman R *Wildlife of the Somerset Levels.* Somerset County Council
Dony J G, Jury S L & Perring F H 1974. *English Names of Wild Flowers.* Botanical Society of the Br. Is.
Drake M 2004. Water and Wildlife on the Levels. *Proc. SANHS* Vol 146, 173-176
Duff A 1993. *Beetles of Somerset.* Som. Arch. Nat. Hist. Soc.

Eales C. 2004. Mid to late Holocene changes in the Environment in the Sedgemoor Valley, Somerset Levels. *PhD Thesis.* Bath Spa University College
English Nature 1997. *Somerset Levels and Moors Natural Area: a nature conservation profile.* English Nature

Fitter R & Manuel R 1986 *Collins Field Guide to Freshwater Life.* Collins
Friday L E 1988 *A Key to the Adults of British Water Beetles.* AIDGAP Field Studies Council

Gillings S 2003 Night feeding in Golden Plovers and Lapwing *BTO News* 248 14-15
Green P R, Green I P & Crouch G A 1997. *The Atlas Flora of Somerset.* Published by the authors
Greshon S 2004 The plant life of ditches on the Levels. *Proc. SANHS* Vol 146, 177-182

Haslam S et al. 1982. *British Water Plants.* AIDGAP Field Studies Council
Hawke C J & P V Jose 1996. *Reedbed Management Handbook.* Royal Society for the Protection of Birds

Hayward J 2004 new ed. *A new key to Wild Flowers*. Cambridge University Press, AIDGAP Field Studies Council

Hill-Cottingham P 1989. *Somerset Ferns a Field Guide*. SANHS Aspects of Somerset, Natural History Series No1

Hill-Cottingham P 2003. The life cycle of the Shining Ram's-horn Snail *Segmentina nitida*. *Bristol Naturalists' Society Nature in Avon* Vol 63

Hill-Cottingham P 2004. The ecology of the Shining Ram's-horn *Segmentina nitida* (M,ller) 1774 on Catcott North reserve (part of a SSSI on the Somerset Levels and Moors) to determine strategies for its conservation. *PhD Thesis Open University*

Hill-Cottingham P 2005. Conservation of a rare snail *Segmentina nitida* Shining Ram's-horn: problems and possible solutions. Proc SANHS Vol 146, 186-190

Hope-Simpson J F et al. 1963. Plant communities on Shapwick Heath, Somerset. *Proc. Brist. Nat. Soc.* 30 (4) pp343-351

Hope-Simpson, J. F. 1949-1963 Annual reports on Sharpham Moor Plot. *Handbook of the Society for the Promotion of Nature Reserves*

Hume R 1997. *The Shell Easy Bird Guide*. Silverdale Books

Hume R 2002. RSPB Birds of Britain and Europe. Dorling Kindersley

Jermy A G & Tutin T G 1968. *British Sedges*. Botanical Society of the Br.Is

Jermy A G & Camus J 1991. *The Illustrated Field Guide to Ferns and Allied Plants of the British Isles*. Natural History Museum Publications

Jones-Walters L M 1989. *Keys to the families of British Spiders*. AIDGAP Field Studies Council

Kerney M P & Cameron R A D 1979. *A Field Guide to the Land Snails of Britain and North-west Europe*. Collins

Killeen I, Aldridge D & Oliver G 2004. *Freshwater Bivalves of Britain and Europe*. AIDGAP Field Studies Council

Lewis S 1055. *The Breeding Birds of Somerset and their Eggs*. Ilfracombe, Stockwell. Facsimile, Wateringbury 2002 P Blest

Macan T T 1977. *A key to the British Fresh- and Brackish-Water Gastropods*. Freshwater Biological Association No.13

Macquitty M 1996. *Amazing Bugs*. Dorling Kindersley

Manning S A (1979) *Nature in the West Country*. World's Work

Mitchell A 1974 *A Field Guide to the Trees of Britain and Northern Europe*. Collins

Neal E 1986. *The Natural History of Badgers*. Guild Publishing

Palmer E M & Ballance D K 1968. *The Birds of Somerset*. Longmans

Rix G M 2003. The history of Sharpham Moor Plot. *Proc. SANHS* Vol 145, 195-199

Rix G M & Hill-Cottingham P 2001 Predation of freshwater snails by a leech *Glossiphonia heteroclita*. *Proc. SANHS* Vol 145, 191-193

Roberts M J 1995. *Collins Field Guide to Spiders of Britain and Northern Europe*. Collins

Shirt D B 1987. *British Red Data Books 2 Insects*. Nature Conservancy Council

Somerset Ornithological Society 1988. *Birds of Somerset*. Allan Sutton

Stace C 1991. *New Flora of the British Isles*. Cambridge

Sterry P 1997. *Collins Complete British Wildlife Photoguide*. Collins

Storer B 1972. *Sedgemoor: Its History and Natural History*. David & Charles

Storer B 1985. *The Natural History of the Somerset Levels*. The Dovecote Press Ltd. Dorset.

Sutherland P & Nicolson A 1986. *Wetland Life in the Somerset Levels*. Michael Joseph

Svensson L et.al. [date?] *Collins Bird Guide*. Collins

Tilling S M 1987. *A Key to the Major Groups of Terrestrial Invertebrates*. AIDGAP Field Studies Council

Trump D & Ovenden G 1999. Nocturnal Movements of Wintering Wildfowl and Waders on the Somerset Levels and Moors January to March. *FRCA Western Region*.

Williams R & R 1992. *The Somerset Levels*. Ex Libris Books

Yalden D & Morris P 1990. *The Analysis of Owl Pellets*. The Mammal Society

THE NATURALISTS' HANDBOOKS (Richmond Publishing Company)

1 *Insects on Nettles* B N K Davis
2 *Grasshoppers* V K Brown
3 *Solitary Wasps* P F Yeo & S A Corbet
4 *Insects and Thistles* M Redfern
5 *Hoverflies* F S Gilbert
6 *Bumblebees* O E Prys-Jones & S A Corbet
7 *Dragonflies* P L Miller
8 *Ground Beetles* T G Forsythe
9 *Animals on Seaweed* P J Hayward
10 *Ladybirds* M Majerus & P Kearns
11 *Aphid Predators* G E Rotheray
12 *Animals of the Surface Film* M Guthrie

13 *Mayflies* J Harker
14 *Mosquitoes* K R Snow
15 *Insects, Plants and Microclimate* D M Unwin & S A Corbet
16 *Weevils* M G Morris
17 *Plant Galls* M Redfern & R R Askew
18 *Insects on Cabbages and Oilseed Rape* W D J Kirk
19 *Pollution Monitoring with Lichens* D H S Richardson
20 *Microscopic Life in Sphagnum* M Hingley
21 *Animals of the Sandy Shores* P J Hayward

22 *Animals under Logs and Stones* C P Wheater & H J Read
23 *Blowflies* Z Erzinclioglu
24 *Ants* G J Skinner & G W Allen
25 *Thrips* W D J Kirk
26 *Insects on Dock Plants* D T Salt & B Whittaker
27 *Insects on Cherry Trees* S R Leather & K P Bland
28 *Studying Invertebrates* C P Wheater & P A Cook

The Field Studies Council also produces charts and other AIDGAP keys on a range of plants and animals.
More scientific books on the identification of aquatic animals are published by the Freshwater Biological Society and others covering terrestrial habitats are published by the Linnaean Society.

Index of Somerset Place Names

235

Relevant Ordnance Survey 1:25 000 Explorer maps

Index of Common Names of Species

Index of Scientific Names of Species